Grade 6

CURRICULUM

Spelling
PRACTICE BOOK

Macmillan
McGraw-Hill

The *McGraw-Hill* Companies

Macmillan
McGraw-Hill

Published by Macmillan/McGraw-Hill, of McGraw-Hill Education, a division of The McGraw-Hill Companies, Inc.,
Two Penn Plaza, New York, New York 10121.

Printed in the United States of America

1 2 3 4 5 6 7 8 9 10 006 09 08 07 06 05

Contents

Unit 2 • Saving the Day

Unit 3 • Great Ideas

© Macmillan/McGraw-Hill

Unit 4 • Achievements

Unit 5 • Turning Points

Unit 6 • Yesterday, Today, and Tomoorrow

Name_____

Fold back the paper along the dotted line. Write the words in the blanks as they are read aloud. When you finish the test, unfold the paper. Use the list at the right to correct any spelling mistakes.

1. _____
2. _____
3. _____
4. _____
5. _____
6. _____
7. _____
8. _____
9. _____
10. _____
11. _____
12. _____
13. _____
14. _____
15. _____
16. _____
17. _____
18. _____
19. _____

Review Words 20. _____

21. _____

22. _____

Challenge Words 23. _____

24. _____

25. _____

1. gram
2. clash
3. dense
4. dread
5. prank
6. strict
7. drill
8. swan
9. prod
10. shrunk
11. scuff
12. clutch
13. threat
14. dwell
15. fund
16. text
17. rank
18. brink
19. mock
20. plaid
21. stuff
22. batch
23. sense
24. guest
25. cleanse

At Home: Help the student practice the words he or she missed to prepare for the Posttest.

Name_____

Using the Word Study Steps

1. LOOK at the word.

2. SAY the word aloud.

3. STUDY the letters in the word.

4. WRITE the word.

5. CHECK the word.
Did you spell the word right?
If not, go back to step 1.

Find Rhyming Words

Circle the word in each row that rhymes with the spelling word on the left.

1. drill	drink	still	swell
2. threat	pet	treat	three
3. rank	rant	blank	rink
4. shrunk	shriek	rung	trunk
5. fund	run	stunned	funk
6. gram	grant	cram	train
7. dense	fence	dentist	ease
8. mock	stick	moist	lock
9. plaid	pleat	said	glad
10. clash	splash	class	juice

Write a poem of at least 4 lines. Include two of the spelling words in your poem.

_____

_____

_____

_____

At Home: Review the Word Study Steps to help the student spell new words.

Name_____

gram	prank	prod	threat	rank
clash	strict	shrunk	dwell	brink
dense	drill	scuff	fund	mock
dread	swan	clutch	text	plaid

Write the spelling words with each of the spelling patterns.

Short *a* spelled:

a

1. _____

2. _____

3. _____

4. _____

ai

5. _____

Short *e* spelled:

e

6. _____

7. _____

8. _____

ea

9. _____

10. _____

Short *i* spelled:

i

11. _____

12. _____

13. _____

Short *o* spelled:

a

14. _____

o

15. _____

16. _____

Short *u* spelled:

u

17. _____

18. _____

19. _____

20. _____

Name_____

gram	prank	prod	threat	rank
clash	strict	shrunk	dwell	brink
dense	drill	scuff	fund	mock
dread	swan	clutch	text	plaid

Definitions

Write the spelling word that matches each definition.

1. a unit of measurement _____

2. the edge or verge _____

3. to brood _____

4. status _____

5. words on a page _____

6. a joke or a trick _____

Sentence Completion

Fill in the blank with the appropriate spelling word.

7. All the students in the sixth grade participated in a _____ rescue mission.

8. Our team wore _____ shirts with khaki pants.

9. We used a _____ to make a wooden raft.

10. We floated over the pond where we saw the _____ yesterday.

11. The _____ of drowning in such shallow water was unlikely.

12. The underbrush was so _____ it was hard to walk through it.

Name_____

Proofreading Activity

There are five spelling mistakes in this story. Circle the misspelled words. Write the words correctly on the lines below.

At midnight, I awoke to find the rain outside dripping in through my bedroom window. I put on my plade bathrobe and walked outside to see if I could stop it. I was surprised to see that the land around my house was covered in dence fog. As I was trying to prodd the window closed, I thought of the thret of being stranded in my house alone for days. This scared me so much that I forgot about the window and ran back into my house, full of dred.

1. _____

2. _____

3. _____

4. _____

5. _____

Writing Activity

Scary experiences can be fun to read about or write about. Do you like to read about such adventures? Write about a scary adventure. Use five spelling words in your writing.

_____

_____

_____

_____

_____

_____

_____

_____

Name_____

Look at the words in each set below. One word in each set is spelled correctly. Use a pencil to fill in the circle next to the correct word. Before you begin, look at the sample set of words. Sample A has been done for you. Do Sample B by yourself. When you are sure you know what to do, you may go on with the rest of the page.

Sample A:
- Ⓐ lump
- Ⓑ lumpe
- Ⓒ lumpp
- Ⓓ luump

Sample B:
- Ⓔ tacke
- Ⓕ taak
- Ⓖ tack
- Ⓗ takk

1.
- Ⓐ gram
- Ⓑ gramm
- Ⓒ grame
- Ⓓ gremm

2.
- Ⓔ clashe
- Ⓕ claash
- Ⓖ clash
- Ⓗ clahsh

3.
- Ⓐ denss
- Ⓑ dens
- Ⓒ dehns
- Ⓓ dense

4.
- Ⓔ dred
- Ⓕ dread
- Ⓖ dreade
- Ⓗ drede

5.
- Ⓐ prank
- Ⓑ pranke
- Ⓒ prenk
- Ⓓ praank

6.
- Ⓔ stricte
- Ⓕ strockt
- Ⓖ strekt
- Ⓗ strict

7.
- Ⓐ dril
- Ⓑ drill
- Ⓒ drile
- Ⓓ drihl

8.
- Ⓔ swan
- Ⓕ swon
- Ⓖ swahn
- Ⓗ swane

9.
- Ⓐ prode
- Ⓑ prod
- Ⓒ prodd
- Ⓓ prode

10.
- Ⓔ shrunke
- Ⓕ shruhnk
- Ⓖ shrenk
- Ⓗ shrunk

11.
- Ⓐ scuf
- Ⓑ scufe
- Ⓒ scuff
- Ⓓ scof

12.
- Ⓔ clutch
- Ⓕ cluch
- Ⓖ cluche
- Ⓗ clutche

13.
- Ⓐ thret
- Ⓑ thrat
- Ⓒ threate
- Ⓓ threat

14.
- Ⓔ dwel
- Ⓕ dwele
- Ⓖ dwell
- Ⓗ dwal

15.
- Ⓐ fund
- Ⓑ funde
- Ⓒ fundd
- Ⓓ fuund

16.
- Ⓔ texte
- Ⓕ texet
- Ⓖ text
- Ⓗ tixt

17.
- Ⓐ rank
- Ⓑ ranke
- Ⓒ renke
- Ⓓ renk

18.
- Ⓔ brink
- Ⓕ brinke
- Ⓖ briink
- Ⓗ brinkk

19.
- Ⓐ moock
- Ⓑ mocke
- Ⓒ mock
- Ⓓ moke

20.
- Ⓔ plad
- Ⓕ plaid
- Ⓖ pladd
- Ⓗ plade

Name _____

Fold back the paper along the dotted line. Write the words in the blanks as they are read aloud. When you finish the test, unfold the paper. Use the list at the right to correct any spelling mistakes.

1. _____	**1.** slope
2. _____	**2.** acute
3. _____	**3.** remote
4. _____	**4.** bathe
5. _____	**5.** gaze
6. _____	**6.** rhyme
7. _____	**7.** keen
8. _____	**8.** tile
9. _____	**9.** fuse
10. _____	**10.** bleach
11. _____	**11.** loan
12. _____	**12.** tote
13. _____	**13.** foal
14. _____	**14.** foe
15. _____	**15.** coax
16. _____	**16.** bleak
17. _____	**17.** cue
18. _____	**18.** pave
19. _____	**19.** meek
20. _____	**20.** shrine
Review Words 21. _____	**21.** grasp
22. _____	**22.** dread
23. _____	**23.** shrunk
Challenge Words 24. _____	**24.** trait
25. _____	**25.** capsule

At Home: Help the student practice the words he or she missed to prepare for the Posttest.

Name

Using the Word Study Steps

1. LOOK at the word.

2. SAY the word aloud.

3. STUDY the letters in the word.

4. WRITE the word.

5. CHECK the word.
Did you spell the word right?
If not, go back to step 1.

Find the Words

Find and circle the spelling words in the puzzle below. The words will be found from left to right, or top to bottom.

```
A s l o p e A C b f t o t e b l e a k m E f O f
T H R I E k c U a u S U t E L O T c u e T o T o
H r h y m e o P t s h r i n e H W u R e p a v e
R I A b l e a c h e U S l o a n I t S k T I U N
E N A C D n x r e m o t e Z g a z e R L S M A O
```

Make a Puzzle

Make up a puzzle of your own using the space on this page. Give it to someone else to solve. Be sure to use at least five spelling words in your puzzle.

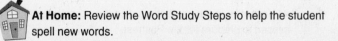

At Home: Review the Word Study Steps to help the student spell new words.

Name_____

slope	gaze	fuse	foal	cue
acute	rhyme	bleach	foe	pave
remote	keen	loan	coax	meek
bathe	tile	tote	bleak	shrine

Write the spelling words with each of the spelling patterns below.

Long *a* spelled:

a_e

1. _____

2. _____

3. _____

Long *e* spelled:

ee

4. _____

5. _____

ea

6. _____

7. _____

Long *i* spelled:

y

8. _____

i_e

9. _____

10. _____

Long *o* spelled

o_e

11. _____

12. _____

13. _____

oa

14. _____

15. _____

16. _____

oe

17. _____

Long *u* spelled

u_e

18. _____

19. _____

ue

20. _____

slope	gaze	fuse	foal	cue
acute	rhyme	bleach	foe	pave
remote	keen	loan	coax	meek
bathe	tile	tote	bleak	shrine

Synonyms

A synonym is a word that means the same as another word. Write the spelling word that matches each synonym.

1. carry _____

2. stare _____

3. enthusiastic _____

4. signal _____

5. distant _____

6. colt _____

Antonyms

An antonym is a word that means the opposite of another word. Write the spelling word that matches each antonym.

7. friend _____

8. separate _____

9. strong _____

10. rise _____

11. mild _____

12. lively _____

Name_____

There are five spelling mistakes in this paragraph. Circle the misspelled words. Write the words correctly on the lines below.

When Randy is left to take care of his little brother, they play at being explorers. Randy takes his horse, his brother takes his fole, and together they paive the way into a forgotten city. When they reach the tyle floor of the bathroom, the room becomes an ancient shryn. Playtime makes it much easier for Randy to coks his brother to sleep.

1. _____

2. _____

3. _____

4. _____

5. _____

Writing Activity

Have you ever played at being an explorer? What did you do and where did you go on your explorer's expedition? Write a letter to a friend describing such an adventure as if it were real. Use five spelling words.

_____

_____

_____

_____

_____

_____

_____

_____

Name_____

Look at the words in each set below. One word in each set is spelled correctly. Use a pencil to fill in the circle next to the correct word. Before you begin, look at the sample set of words. Sample A has been done for you. Do Sample B by yourself. When you are sure you know what to do, you may go on with the rest of the page.

Sample A:
- Ⓐ doom
- Ⓑ dume
- Ⓒ duum
- Ⓓ doome

Sample B:
- Ⓔ taik
- Ⓕ taak
- Ⓖ take
- Ⓗ tehk

1.
- Ⓐ slopp
- Ⓑ slope
- Ⓒ sloop
- Ⓓ slohp

6.
- Ⓔ rime
- Ⓕ rhyme
- Ⓖ rhime
- Ⓗ ryme

11.
- Ⓐ lon
- Ⓑ lone
- Ⓒ loan
- Ⓓ lohn

16.
- Ⓔ bleek
- Ⓕ bleke
- Ⓖ blek
- Ⓗ bleak

2.
- Ⓔ acoot
- Ⓕ acut
- Ⓖ acyute
- Ⓗ acute

7.
- Ⓐ kene
- Ⓑ keen
- Ⓒ ken
- Ⓓ kein

12.
- Ⓔ tote
- Ⓕ tott
- Ⓖ toat
- Ⓗ toht

17.
- Ⓐ cyu
- Ⓑ cue
- Ⓒ coo
- Ⓓ cu

3.
- Ⓐ remote
- Ⓑ reemote
- Ⓒ reemot
- Ⓓ remot

8.
- Ⓔ tile
- Ⓕ til
- Ⓖ tihl
- Ⓗ tale

13.
- Ⓐ foal
- Ⓑ fole
- Ⓒ fohl
- Ⓓ foll

18.
- Ⓔ pav
- Ⓕ paive
- Ⓖ pave
- Ⓗ paiv

4.
- Ⓔ bayth
- Ⓕ bethe
- Ⓖ bathe
- Ⓗ beth

9.
- Ⓐ foose
- Ⓑ fus
- Ⓒ fuse
- Ⓓ fyuse

14.
- Ⓔ fo
- Ⓕ fow
- Ⓖ foh
- Ⓗ foe

19.
- Ⓐ meak
- Ⓑ meke
- Ⓒ mek
- Ⓓ meek

5.
- Ⓐ gaze
- Ⓑ gass
- Ⓒ geze
- Ⓓ gez

10.
- Ⓔ bleech
- Ⓕ bleach
- Ⓖ bleche
- Ⓗ blech

15.
- Ⓐ coxe
- Ⓑ coax
- Ⓒ cohx
- Ⓓ cokes

20.
- Ⓔ shrin
- Ⓕ shrine
- Ⓖ shrihn
- Ⓗ shriin

Name _____

Fold back the paper along the dotted line. Write the words in the blanks as they are read aloud. When you finish the test, unfold the paper. Use the list at the right to correct any spelling mistakes.

1. _____
2. _____
3. _____
4. _____
5. _____
6. _____
7. _____
8. _____
9. _____
10. _____
11. _____
12. _____
13. _____
14. _____
15. _____
16. _____
17. _____
18. _____
19. _____
20. _____

Review Words 21. _____

22. _____

23. _____

Challenge Words 24. _____

25. _____

1. reins
2. freight
3. siege
4. yield
5. review
6. foreign
7. shield
8. ceiling
9. retrieve
10. grieve
11. sleigh
12. seize
13. belief
14. neither
15. reign
16. relieve
17. niece
18. eighty
19. wield
20. diesel
21. gaze
22. tile
23. bleach
24. receipt
25. leisure

© Macmillan/McGraw-Hill

 At Home: Help the student practice the words he or she missed to prepare for the Posttest.

Time For Kids • **Grade 6/Unit 1** 13

Using the Word Study Steps

1. LOOK at the word.

2. SAY the word aloud.

3. STUDY the letters in the word.

4. WRITE the word.

5. CHECK the word.
  Did you spell the word right?
  If not, go back to step 1.

What's Missing?

Fill in the missing letters to form spelling words.

1. ____ei____e

2. ____ei____ing

3. re____ ____ ____ ____

4. ____ ____ghty

5. ____ie____e

6. ____ ____ield

7. ____ie____ ____

8. ____ ____ie____e

9. ____ei____n

10. sl____ ____ ____ ____

11. di____ ____ ____ ____

12. rei____s

13. nei____ ____ ____ ____

14. nie____ ____

15. ____ ____lief

16. ____ ____lie____e

17. ____ ____eight

18. yie____ ____

19. f____ ____ ____ ____ ____ ____

20. ____ ____ ____ ____ ____eve

Write the Words

Use the lines below to practice writing the spelling words.

_____ _____ _____ _____

_____ _____ _____ _____

_____ _____ _____ _____

_____ _____ _____ _____

_____ _____ _____ _____

At Home: Review the Word Study Steps to help the student spell new words.

© Macmillan/McGraw-Hill

Name_____

reins	review	retrieve	belief	niece
freight	foreign	grieve	neither	eighty
siege	shield	sleigh	reign	wield
yield	ceiling	seize	relieve	diesel

Write the spelling words with each of the spelling patterns below.

ei

1. _____
2. _____
3. _____
4. _____
5. _____
6. _____
7. _____
8. _____
9. _____

ie

10. _____
11. _____
12. _____
13. _____
14. _____
15. _____
16. _____
17. _____
18. _____
19. _____
20. _____

Alphabetical Order

Use the lines below to write the spelling words in alphabetical order.

_____ _____ _____ _____

_____ _____ _____ _____

_____ _____ _____ _____

_____ _____ _____ _____

_____ _____ _____ _____

Name_____

reins	review	retrieve	belief	niece
freight	foreign	grieve	neither	eighty
siege	shield	sleigh	reign	wield
yield	ceiling	seize	relieve	diesel

Sentence Completion

Fill in the blank with the appropriate spelling word.

1. Many of the everyday objects we use were invented in _____ countries.

2. The _____ engine was named after its inventor.

3. Water skiis were invented over _____ years ago.

4. My _____ is working on an invention for my brother, her father.

5. _____ of the Wright brothers gave up until they could fly.

6. The driver held the _____ as he drove the horses.

Synonyms

Write the spelling word that is a synonym for each word below.

7. rule _____

8. mourn _____

9. grab _____

10. fetch _____

11. help _____

12. surrender _____

Name _____

There are five spelling mistakes in this letter. Circle the misspelled words. Write the words correctly on the lines below.

Dear Aunt Anita,

My vacation in Colorado is very enjoyable. We certainly are lucky that my father invented a new type of snow-making machine! Since I arrived, it feels like I have skied the mountain aty times. Last night, my mother and I took an old-fashioned sliegh ride in the snow. I even was allowed to hold the rains. When I pulled them close to me, the horses would yeild. It was loads of fun. I think tomorrow we are going to go sledding. I'll tell you all about it when I get home. I miss you.

Your neice,

Julie

1. _____

2. _____

3. _____

4. _____

5. _____

Writing Activity

Julie's father brought her family to Colorado because he invented a special kind of snow-making machine. What other inventions might require someone to go away on business? Write a postcard as if you were on such a trip. Use five spelling words in your postcard.

_____

_____

_____

_____

_____

_____

Name_____

Look at the words in each set below. One word in each set is spelled correctly. Use a pencil to fill in the circle next to the correct word. Before you begin, look at the sample set of words. Sample A has been done for you. Do Sample B by yourself. When you are sure you know what to do, you may go on with the rest of the page.

Sample A:
- Ⓐ tried
- Ⓑ tryed
- Ⓒ tride
- Ⓓ treid

Sample B:
- Ⓔ recieve
- Ⓕ reiceve
- Ⓖ receive
- Ⓗ riecive

1.
- Ⓐ reins
- Ⓑ reinz
- Ⓒ riens
- Ⓓ rienz

2.
- Ⓔ frieght
- Ⓕ freight
- Ⓖ freit
- Ⓗ friet

3.
- Ⓐ seige
- Ⓑ siege
- Ⓒ sieg
- Ⓓ seig

4.
- Ⓔ yeild
- Ⓕ eild
- Ⓖ yield
- Ⓗ ield

5.
- Ⓐ reivew
- Ⓑ review
- Ⓒ rievew
- Ⓓ reveiw

6.
- Ⓔ foriegn
- Ⓕ foreign
- Ⓖ forein
- Ⓗ forien

7.
- Ⓐ sheild
- Ⓑ shield
- Ⓒ shielde
- Ⓓ sheilde

8.
- Ⓔ cieling
- Ⓕ celeing
- Ⓖ ceiling
- Ⓗ celieng

9.
- Ⓐ retreive
- Ⓑ reitreve
- Ⓒ retrieve
- Ⓓ rietreve

10.
- Ⓔ greive
- Ⓕ grevie
- Ⓖ grevei
- Ⓗ grieve

11.
- Ⓐ sleigh
- Ⓑ sliegh
- Ⓒ slei
- Ⓓ slie

12.
- Ⓔ seize
- Ⓕ sieze
- Ⓖ sezie
- Ⓗ sezei

13.
- Ⓐ beilef
- Ⓑ bielef
- Ⓒ belief
- Ⓓ beleif

14.
- Ⓔ neither
- Ⓕ niether
- Ⓖ netheir
- Ⓗ nethier

15.
- Ⓐ riegn
- Ⓑ reign
- Ⓒ rieghn
- Ⓓ reighn

16.
- Ⓔ relieve
- Ⓕ reilive
- Ⓖ rielive
- Ⓗ eleive

17.
- Ⓐ neice
- Ⓑ necie
- Ⓒ niece
- Ⓓ necei

18.
- Ⓔ eigty
- Ⓕ iegty
- Ⓖ eighty
- Ⓗ eigthy

19.
- Ⓐ weild
- Ⓑ wield
- Ⓒ weilde
- Ⓓ wielde

20.
- Ⓔ deisel
- Ⓕ deseil
- Ⓖ desiel
- Ⓗ diesel

Fold back the paper along the dotted line. Write the words in the blanks as they are read aloud. When you finish the test, unfold the paper. Use the list at the right to correct any spelling mistakes.

1. _____
2. _____
3. _____
4. _____
5. _____
6. _____
7. _____
8. _____
9. _____
10. _____
11. _____
12. _____
13. _____
14. _____
15. _____
16. _____
17. _____
18. _____
19. _____
20. _____

Review Words 21. _____
22. _____
23. _____

Challenge Words 24. _____
25. _____

1. search
2. starve
3. thorn
4. reward
5. sparkle
6. bargain
7. parched
8. pursue
9. servant
10. torch
11. earnest
12. mourn
13. fierce
14. pierce
15. urge
16. warf
17. court
18. weird
19. veer
20. burnt
21. freight
22. yield
23. seize
24. sphere
25. aeronautics

At Home: Help the student practice the words he or she missed to prepare for the Posttest.

Name_____

Using the Word Study Steps

1. LOOK at the word.
2. SAY the word aloud.
3. STUDY the letters in the word.
4. WRITE the word.
5. CHECK the word.
   Did you spell the word right?
   If not, go back to step 1.

Alphabetical Order

search	sparkle	servant	fierce	court
starve	bargain	torch	pierce	weird
thorn	parched	earnest	urge	veer
reward	pursue	mourn	wharf	burnt

Write the spelling words in alphabetical order.

1. _____
2. _____
3. _____
4. _____
5. _____
6. _____
7. _____
8. _____
9. _____
10. _____

11. _____
12. _____
13. _____
14. _____
15. _____
16. _____
17. _____
18. _____
19. _____
20. _____

At Home: Review the Word Study Steps to help the student spell new words.

Name_____

search	sparkle	servant	fierce	court
starve	bargain	torch	pierce	weird
thorn	parched	earnest	urge	veer
reward	pursue	mourn	wharf	burnt

Write the spelling words with each of the spelling patterns below.

är spelled:

ar

1. _____

2. _____

3. _____

4. _____

îr spelled:

ier

5. _____

6. _____

eir

7. _____

eer

8. _____

ôr spelled:

or

9. _____

10. _____

ar

11. _____

12. _____

our

13. _____

14. _____

ûr spelled:

ear

15. _____

16. _____

ur

17. _____

18. _____

19. _____

er

20. _____

Name_____

search	sparkle	servant	fierce	court
starve	bargain	torch	pierce	weird
thorn	parched	earnest	urge	veer
reward	pursue	mourn	wharf	burnt

Analogies

Write the spelling word that completes each analogy.

1. **Dock** is to _____ as **park** is to **garage**.

2. **Open** is to **close** as **retreat** is to _____.

3. **Thirst** is to **drink** as _____ is to **eat**.

4. **Teacher** is to **classroom** as **judge** is to _____.

5. **Laugh** is to **chortle** as _____ is to **grieve**.

Completions

Use a spelling word to complete the following sentences.

6. He lost control of his car and it started to _____ off the road.

7. She offered a _____ to anyone with information about their lost family heirloom.

8. Our customs seemed _____ to Uta.

9. In Egypt, it is common to _____ with the street vendors.

10. The _____ weather conditions allow them to spend more time at home, inside with their families.

More Analogies

Write some analogies of your own on the lines below. Use at least one spelling word in each analogy.

11. _____

12. _____

There are five spelling mistakes in this story. Circle the misspelled words. Write the words correctly on the lines below.

Long ago when James was a young boy, he worked as a mayor's servent and lived in a shed behind their mansion. Late one night, the mayor's wife came to James's door with an ernest request. Her husband had gone for a walk and had not yet returned hours later. She didn't need to irge James to find her husband. James took a tortch and went to serch for him. Hours later, James found and rescued the mayor. The next day the news was all over the small town, and James became a hero. Over the years, the story of James's adventure grew until it became a grand tale.

1. _____

2. _____

3. _____

4. _____

5. _____

Writing Activity

How might the story of James's simple adventure have changed over the years? Write a tale that might have grown from it. Use five spelling words in your story.

_____

_____

_____

_____

_____

_____

Name_____

Look at the words in each set below. One word in each set is spelled correctly. Use a pencil to fill in the circle next to the correct word. Before you begin, look at the sample set of words. Sample A has been done for you. Do Sample B by yourself. When you are sure you know what to do, you may go on with the rest of the page.

Sample A:
Ⓐ sport
Ⓑ spart
Ⓒ sporte
Ⓓ spohrt

Sample B:
Ⓔ bork
Ⓕ barke
Ⓖ bark
Ⓗ bohrk

1. Ⓐ search
   Ⓑ sirch
   Ⓒ sertch
   Ⓓ seartch

2. Ⓔ starv
   Ⓕ starfe
   Ⓖ starve
   Ⓗ storv

3. Ⓐ thorne
   Ⓑ thorn
   Ⓒ thornn
   Ⓓ thohrn

4. Ⓔ reworde
   Ⓕ reeward
   Ⓖ reeword
   Ⓗ reward

5. Ⓐ sporkle
   Ⓑ sparkle
   Ⓒ sporkel
   Ⓓ sparkel

6. Ⓔ bargain
   Ⓕ borgen
   Ⓖ bargen
   Ⓗ borgain

7. Ⓐ partched
   Ⓑ portched
   Ⓒ parched
   Ⓓ porched

8. Ⓔ pursoo
   Ⓕ porsoo
   Ⓖ pursue
   Ⓗ porsue

9. Ⓐ survunt
   Ⓑ survent
   Ⓒ servant
   Ⓓ servent

10. Ⓔ tortch
    Ⓕ torche
    Ⓖ torch
    Ⓗ tohrch

11. Ⓐ ernest
    Ⓑ erneast
    Ⓒ ernast
    Ⓓ earnest

12. Ⓔ mourn
    Ⓕ morne
    Ⓖ moarn
    Ⓗ moorn

13. Ⓐ feerce
    Ⓑ feirce
    Ⓒ fierce
    Ⓓ ferce

14. Ⓔ peirce
    Ⓕ pearce
    Ⓖ pierce
    Ⓗ perce

15. Ⓐ urge
    Ⓑ urg
    Ⓒ oorge
    Ⓓ erge

16. Ⓔ worf
    Ⓕ wharf
    Ⓖ warf
    Ⓗ whorf

17. Ⓐ cort
    Ⓑ corte
    Ⓒ court
    Ⓓ coart

18. Ⓔ wierd
    Ⓕ weerd
    Ⓖ weird
    Ⓗ werde

19. Ⓐ vier
    Ⓑ veir
    Ⓒ veer
    Ⓓ vere

20. Ⓔ burnet
    Ⓕ burnt
    Ⓖ boornt
    Ⓗ burnte

Name _____

Fold back the paper along the dotted line. Write the words in the blanks as they are read aloud. When you finish the test, unfold the paper. Use the list at the right to correct any spelling mistakes.

1. _____
2. _____
3. _____
4. _____
5. _____
6. _____
7. _____
8. _____
9. _____
10. _____
11. _____
12. _____
13. _____
14. _____
15. _____
16. _____
17. _____
18. _____
19. _____
20. _____

Review Words 21. _____
22. _____
23. _____

Challenge Words 24. _____
25. _____

1. heartbeat
2. northwest
3. seaweed
4. eyelid
5. seashell
6. twenty-five
7. wading pool
8. nearsighted
9. brother-in-law
10. old-fashioned
11. full-time
12. windshield
13. watermelon
14. science fiction
15. self-respect
16. flashbulb
17. after-school
18. teenager
19. fingernail
20. question mark
21. fierce
22. urge
23. bargain
24. barbed wire
25. firece escape

At Home: Help the student practice the words he or she missed to prepare for the Posttest.

Name_____

Using the Word Study Steps

1. LOOK at the word.

2. SAY the word aloud.

3. STUDY the letters in the word.

4. WRITE the word.

5. CHECK the word.
   Did you spell the word right?
   If not, go back to step 1.

Finish the Word

Complete each word below to form a spelling word.

1. north_____

2. self-_____

3. _____ pool

4. _____bulb

5. full_____

6. _____ mark

7. near_____

8. _____ager

9. _____nail

10. wind_____

11. _____beat

12. _____-in-law

13. _____shell

14. _____five

15. _____weed

16. old-_____

17. _____ fiction

18. eye_____

19. _____melon

20. _____-school

Use Compound Words

Write two sentences on the lines below. Use a compound word in each sentence.

21. _____

22. _____

At Home: Review the Word Study Steps to help the student spell new words.

© Macmillan/McGraw-Hill

Name_____

heartbeat	seashell	brother-in-law	watermelon	after-school
northwest	twenty-five	old-fashioned	science fiction	teenager
seaweed	wading pool	full-time	self-respect	fingernail
eyelid	nearsighted	windshield	flashbulb	question mark

Sort each spelling word according to whether it is written as one word, as two words, or with a hyphen. Write each word on the appropriate line below.

One Word:

1. _____

2. _____

3. _____

4. _____

5. _____

6. _____

7. _____

8. _____

9. _____

10. _____

11. _____

Two Words:

12. _____

13. _____

14. _____

Hyphenated:

15. _____

16. _____

17. _____

18. _____

19. _____

20. _____

Write two sentences using as many compound words as you can in each sentence.

21. _____

_____

_____

22. _____

_____

_____

Name _____

heartbeat	seashell	brother-in-law	watermelon	after-school
northwest	twenty-five	old-fashioned	science fiction	teenager
seaweed	wading pool	full-time	self-respect	fingernail
eyelid	nearsighted	windshield	flashbulb	question mark

Finish the Set

Write the spelling word that belongs in each group.

1. pupil, lashes, _____

2. toddler, adult, _____

3. period, comma, _____

4. knuckle, palm, _____

5. three, fourteen, _____

6. antique, classical, _____

7. apple, peach, _____

8. south, east, _____

9. sister, nephew, _____

10. pulse, breathing _____

Write About It

Use one of the sets of words above in a short piece of writing about a topic of your choice.

_____

_____

_____

_____

_____

_____

Name_____

There are five misspelled spelling words in this story. Circle the misspelled words. Write the words correctly on the lines below.

    Manuel lost his glasses at his fulltime job. Manuel is near-sited and so he had great difficulty driving home. He was headed home when suddenly he felt a big bump under his car, and something red splattered against the winsheeld. He thought he had hit an animal, so his hartbeat began to race. He pulled over to the side of the road to see what he had hit. Squinting to get a better look, Manuel let out a chuckle. In the middle of the road was a crushed water-melon.

1. _____

2. _____

3. _____

4. _____

5. _____

Writing Activity

If you were a conservationist, what kind of adventures might you have? Write about a day in the life of a conservationist. Use five spelling words in your writing.

_____

_____

_____

_____

_____

_____

_____

Name_____

Look at the words in each set below. One word in each set is spelled correctly. Use a pencil to fill in the circle next to the correct word. Before you begin, look at the sample set of words. Sample A has been done for you. Do Sample B by yourself. When you are sure you know what to do, you may go on with the rest of the page.

Sample A:
- Ⓐ firsthand
- Ⓑ fursthend
- Ⓒ foorsthand
- Ⓓ fuhrsthand

Sample B:
- Ⓔ bloobery
- Ⓕ blooberry
- Ⓖ blueberry
- Ⓗ bluberry

1.
- Ⓐ heart beat
- Ⓑ heartbeat
- Ⓒ heart-beat
- Ⓓ heartbeet

6.
- Ⓔ twenty-five
- Ⓕ twenty five
- Ⓖ twentyfive
- Ⓗ tuentee-five

11.
- Ⓐ full time
- Ⓑ fulltime
- Ⓒ fultime
- Ⓓ full-time

16.
- Ⓔ flash bulb
- Ⓕ flash-bolb
- Ⓖ flashbulb
- Ⓗ flash-bulb

2.
- Ⓔ north west
- Ⓕ north-west
- Ⓖ northwest
- Ⓗ noorthwest

7.
- Ⓐ wading pool
- Ⓑ wading-pool
- Ⓒ wadingpule
- Ⓓ wadingpool

12.
- Ⓔ windshield
- Ⓕ wind shield
- Ⓖ wind sheeld
- Ⓗ wind-shield

17.
- Ⓐ afterschool
- Ⓑ after-school
- Ⓒ after skool
- Ⓓ after school

3.
- Ⓐ seaweed
- Ⓑ sea weed
- Ⓒ sea-weed
- Ⓓ seewead

8.
- Ⓔ near sited
- Ⓕ nearsited
- Ⓖ nearsighted
- Ⓗ near sighted

13.
- Ⓐ water melon
- Ⓑ water-melon
- Ⓒ watermelon
- Ⓓ wattermellon

18.
- Ⓔ teen-ager
- Ⓕ teen ager
- Ⓖ tenager
- Ⓗ teenager

4.
- Ⓔ eye lid
- Ⓕ eye-lid
- Ⓖ ayelid
- Ⓗ eyelid

9.
- Ⓐ brother in law
- Ⓑ brotherinlaw
- Ⓒ brother in-law
- Ⓓ brother-in-law

14.
- Ⓔ sciencefiction
- Ⓕ science-fiction
- Ⓖ science fiction
- Ⓗ sciense fiction

19.
- Ⓐ finger nail
- Ⓑ finger-nail
- Ⓒ finger nale
- Ⓓ fingernail

5.
- Ⓐ seeshel
- Ⓑ sea-shell
- Ⓒ seashell
- Ⓓ sea shell

10.
- Ⓔ old fashioned
- Ⓕ old-fashoned
- Ⓖ old-fashioned
- Ⓗ oldfashioned

15.
- Ⓐ self-respect
- Ⓑ selfrespect
- Ⓒ self respect
- Ⓓ self respact

20.
- Ⓔ questionmark
- Ⓕ question mark
- Ⓖ queschunmark
- Ⓗ question-mark

© Macmillan/McGraw-Hill

Name_____

Read each sentence. If an underlined word is spelled wrong, fill in the circle that goes with that word. If no word is spelled wrong, fill in the circle below NONE. Read Sample A, and do Sample B.

NONE

A. The <u>twenty-five</u> <u>ernest</u> actors waited patiently for their
      A   B

<u>cue</u> to take the stage.
 C

A. Ⓐ ⬤Ⓑ Ⓒ Ⓓ

NONE

B. I had to <u>search</u> the Internet to <u>retrieve</u> information for
        E   F

my report on the <u>northwest</u>.
             G

B. Ⓔ Ⓕ Ⓖ Ⓗ

NONE

1. The tour group took a <u>sleigh</u> to a <u>remote</u> location to
                 A   B

view an ancient <u>srine</u>.
          C

1. Ⓐ Ⓑ Ⓒ Ⓓ

NONE

2. The 700-page <u>text</u> of the <u>sience fiction</u> novel was <u>dense</u>.
               E   F   G

2. Ⓔ Ⓕ Ⓖ Ⓗ

NONE

3. At the farm, I fed the orphaned <u>fol</u> <u>watermelon</u> so he
                      A   B

would not <u>starve</u>.
        C

3. Ⓐ Ⓑ Ⓒ Ⓓ

NONE

4. I <u>dread</u> the <u>bleak</u> day my pet will die, as I will <u>morn</u> his loss.
    E   F   G

4. Ⓔ Ⓕ Ⓖ Ⓗ

NONE

5. My <u>weird</u> grandmother said I was so dirty I might have
      A

to <u>bayth</u> in <u>bleach</u>.
   B   C

5. Ⓐ Ⓑ Ⓒ Ⓓ

NONE

6. The warriors of the highest <u>rank</u> know how to <u>wield</u> a
                     E   F

sword and hold a <u>shield</u>.
            G

6. Ⓔ Ⓕ Ⓖ Ⓗ

NONE

7. During the carriage ride, I had to <u>seize</u> the <u>reins</u> to
                         A   B

make the horses <u>yeeld</u>.
         C

7. Ⓐ Ⓑ Ⓒ Ⓓ

© Macmillan/McGraw-Hill

NONE

8. At <u>atey</u> years old, my grandmother is very <u>meek</u> and <u>old-fashioned.</u>
   E   F
   G

8. Ⓔ Ⓕ Ⓖ Ⓗ

NONE

9. My <u>brother-in-law</u> played a <u>prank</u> on my <u>niece</u>.
          A   B   C

9. Ⓐ Ⓑ Ⓒ Ⓓ

NONE

10. I tried to <u>coax</u> the <u>swan</u> back into the <u>wading</u> pool.
          E   F   G

10. Ⓔ Ⓕ Ⓖ Ⓗ

NONE

11. The words <u>greeve</u> and <u>relieve</u> <u>rhyme</u>.
              A   B   C

11. Ⓐ Ⓑ Ⓒ Ⓓ

NONE

12. The student who raised the most money for the school <u>funed</u> won a <u>keen</u> <u>reward</u>.
     E   F   G

12. Ⓔ Ⓕ Ⓖ Ⓗ

NONE

13. The truck was carrying a large <u>frate</u> when it began to <u>veer</u> off the road and head into the <u>wharf</u>.
                            A
  B   C

13. Ⓐ Ⓑ Ⓒ Ⓓ

NONE

14. I found <u>neither</u> <u>seaweed</u> nor a <u>seashel</u> on the beach.
          E   F   G

14. Ⓔ Ⓕ Ⓖ Ⓗ

NONE

15. The <u>teenager</u> wore blue <u>sparkle</u> eye shadow on her <u>eyelid</u>.
        A   B   C

15. Ⓐ Ⓑ Ⓒ Ⓓ

NONE

16. She likes to <u>gaze</u> at the <u>fearce</u> light from the <u>torch</u>.
          E   F   G

16. Ⓔ Ⓕ Ⓖ Ⓗ

NONE

17. The <u>near-sighted</u> <u>servant</u> cleaned the <u>seiling</u>.
        A   B   C

17. Ⓐ Ⓑ Ⓒ Ⓓ

NONE

18. Due to a <u>clash</u> over a <u>loan</u>, my friend is now my <u>fo</u>.
         E   F   G

18. Ⓔ Ⓕ Ⓖ Ⓗ

NONE

19. I <u>urge</u> you to be careful when you pick a rose, the <u>thorn</u> might <u>pierce</u> you.
   A
  B   C

19. Ⓐ Ⓑ Ⓒ Ⓓ

NONE

20. <u>After-skool</u>, I would like to <u>persue</u> <u>fulltime</u> work.
     E   F   G

20. Ⓔ Ⓕ Ⓖ Ⓗ

© Macmillan/McGraw-Hill

Name _____

Fold back the paper along the dotted line. Write the words in the blanks as they are read aloud. When you finish the test, unfold the paper. Use the list at the right to correct any spelling mistakes.

1. _____
2. _____
3. _____
4. _____
5. _____
6. _____
7. _____
8. _____
9. _____
10. _____
11. _____
12. _____
13. _____
14. _____
15. _____
16. _____
17. _____
18. _____
19. _____
20. _____

Review Words 21. _____
22. _____
23. _____

Challenge Words 24. _____
25. _____

1. echoes
2. photos
3. data
4. scarves
5. volcanoes
6. shelves
7. media
8. bacteria
9. wolves
10. dominoes
11. solos
12. thieves
13. wives
14. cuffs
15. staffs
16. buffaloes
17. sheriffs
18. tornadoes
19. sopranos
20. loaves
21. old-fashioned
22. windshield
23. question mark
24. halves
25. wharves

At Home: Help the student practice the words he or she missed to prepare for the Posttest.

How Tia Lola Came to Stay (33)
Grade 6/Unit 2

Name_____

Using the Word Study Steps

1. LOOK at the word.
2. SAY the word aloud.
3. STUDY the letters in the word.
4. WRITE the word.
5. CHECK the word.
   Did you spell the word right?
   If not, go back to step 1.

Find the Words

Find and circle the spelling words in the puzzle below.

```
A B M T O R N A D O E S R A H W O L V E S M N P
S H E L V E S D O U C S T T H I E V E S V W R O
O L D M P C S A P P H O T O S V O L C A N O E S
L A I D E U E T D D O M I N O E S O E S M R A N
O S A B U F F A L O E S A R P S H E R I F F S H
S S T A F F S O P E S O P R A N O S E N O E D R
L O A V E S C A R V E S A B N O B A C T E R I A
```

Make a Puzzle

Make up a puzzle of your own using the space on this page. Give it to someone else to solve. Be sure to use at least five spelling words in your puzzle.

At Home: Review the Word Study Steps to help the student spell new words.

Name_____

echoes	photos	data	scarves	volcanoes
shelves	media	bacteria	wolves	dominoes
solos	thieves	wives	cuffs	staffs
buffaloes	sheriffs	tornadoes	sopranos	loaves

Write the spelling words with each of the spelling patterns below.

-oes

1. _____
2. _____
3. _____
4. _____
5. _____

-os

6. _____
7. _____
8. _____

-a

9. _____
10. _____
11. _____

-ves

12. _____
13. _____
14. _____
15. _____
16. _____
17. _____

-ffs

18. _____
19. _____
20. _____

Name_____

echoes	photos	data	scarves	volcanoes
shelves	media	bacteria	wolves	dominoes
solos	thieves	wives	cuffs	staffs
buffaloes	sheriffs	tornadoes	sopranos	loaves

Definitions

Write the spelling word that matches each definition.

1. ways of communication such as television or radio _____

2. animals related to dogs that hunt in packs _____

3. persons who steal _____

4. a game involving tiles with dots _____

5. sound waves meet a large surface and bounce back _____

6. the ends of sleeves that cover the wrists _____

7. flat boards used for storage or display _____

8. parasitic organisms _____

9. persons with the highest singing voice _____

10. images made using a camera _____

11. officers of the law _____

12. information _____

13. cloth worn to keep the neck warm _____

14. sung by one person _____

15. oxen with heavy horns _____

16. destructive whirling winds accompanied by funnel-shaped clouds

_____

Name_____

Proofreading Activity

The day my friend Mickey returned from vacation, he came running over to my house to show me his fotos. He had some incredible pictures. There was one of Mickey herding a group of bufaloes. There was another of him standing on the tops of volcanos. Mickey showed me another picture of him defending himself against a pack of wolfs. The last picture was of him standing firmly on the ground while winds from gigantic tornadose destroyed everything around him.

"Why, Mickey!" I exclaimed "Seems like you had a really amazing vacation."

"No," Mickey said sheepishly. "I spent my whole vacation at my grandmother's house creating these silly pictures on her computer."

1. _____

2. _____

3. _____

4. _____

5. _____

Writing Activity

Have you ever imagined doing something similar to the things that Mickey does in his photos? Write about an adventure you would like to take in your life. Use five spelling words.

_____

_____

_____

_____

_____

_____

Name_____

Look at the words in each set below. One word in each set is spelled correctly. Use a pencil to fill in the circle next to the correct word. Before you begin, look at the sample set of words. Sample A has been done for you. Do Sample B by yourself. When you are sure you know what to do, you may go on with the rest of the page.

Sample A:

Ⓐ potatos
Ⓑ pottatos
Ⓒ potatoes
Ⓓ potattoes

Sample B:

Ⓔ pianos
Ⓕ piannos
Ⓖ pianoes
Ⓗ piannoes

1. Ⓐ echos
   Ⓑ eckos
   Ⓒ echoes
   Ⓓ ekose

6. Ⓔ photoes
   Ⓕ photoss
   Ⓖ fotos
   Ⓗ photos

11. Ⓐ dayta
    Ⓑ data
    Ⓒ datta
    Ⓓ daatta

16. Ⓔ scarfes
    Ⓕ scareves
    Ⓖ scarves
    Ⓗ scarvees

2. Ⓔ volcanoes
   Ⓕ volcanose
   Ⓖ volcanoss
   Ⓗ volkanoes

7. Ⓐ shelfes
   Ⓑ shelves
   Ⓒ shelfs
   Ⓓ schelevs

12. Ⓔ meedia
    Ⓕ midea
    Ⓖ meddia
    Ⓗ media

17. Ⓐ backteria
    Ⓑ bactterria
    Ⓒ bakteria
    Ⓓ bacteria

3. Ⓐ wolfs
   Ⓑ woolves
   Ⓒ woolfes
   Ⓓ wolves

8. Ⓔ dawminoes
   Ⓕ dominos
   Ⓖ dominoes
   Ⓗ dominnoes

13. Ⓐ solos
    Ⓑ sewlos
    Ⓒ colos
    Ⓓ soloz

18. Ⓔ thifes
    Ⓕ theeves
    Ⓖ theives
    Ⓗ thieves

4. Ⓔ wifes
   Ⓕ wives
   Ⓖ wivse
   Ⓗ wavies

9. Ⓐ kuffs
   Ⓑ cufs
   Ⓒ cuffs
   Ⓓ cuffss

14. Ⓔ sttafs
    Ⓕ staves
    Ⓖ staffs
    Ⓗ stafs

19. Ⓐ bufalos
    Ⓑ buffaloes
    Ⓒ bufaloes
    Ⓓ buffalos

5. Ⓐ cherifs
   Ⓑ sherifz
   Ⓒ sheriffs
   Ⓓ sherifs

10. Ⓔ tornados
    Ⓕ tornadoes
    Ⓖ tornadoz
    Ⓗ torrnadoes

15. Ⓐ sopranoes
    Ⓑ soapranos
    Ⓒ sospranoes
    Ⓓ sopranos

20. Ⓔ loaves
    Ⓕ loafs
    Ⓖ lowves
    Ⓗ loafes

© Macmillan/McGraw-Hill

Name_____

Fold back the paper along the dotted line. Write the words in the blanks as they are read aloud. When you finish the test, unfold the paper. Use the list at the right to correct any spelling mistakes.

1. _____   1. sloped
2. _____   2. stifling
3. _____   3. marveled
4. _____   4. sipped
5. _____   5. encouraged
6. _____   6. permitting
7. _____   7. orbiting
8. _____   8. credited
9. _____   9. labored
10. _____   10. patrolling
11. _____   11. referred
12. _____   12. regretting
13. _____   13. totaled
14. _____   14. unraveling
15. _____   15. uttered
16. _____   16. reviving
17. _____   17. glimmering
18. _____   18. accused
19. _____   19. confiding
20. _____   20. hovered

Review Words   21. _____   21. echoes
22. _____   22. shelves
23. _____   23. media

Challenge Words   24. _____   24. interpreted
25. _____   25. swiveling

At Home: Help the student practice the words he or she missed to prepare for the Posttest.

The Night of the Pomegranate   39
Grade 6/Unit 2

© Macmillan/McGraw-Hill

Name_____

Using the Word Study Steps

1. LOOK at the word.

2. SAY the word aloud.

3. STUDY the letters in the word.

4. WRITE the word.

5. CHECK the word.
Did you spell the word right?
If not, go back to step 1.

Missing Letters

Fill in the missing letters to form spelling words.

1. reg ___ ___ ___t ing

2. t ___ ___ ___ ___ ed

3. h ___ ___ ___ ___ ed

4. o ___ ___ ___ ___ ing

5. c ___ ___ ___ ___ ___ ing

6. sl ___ ___ ed

7. en ___ ___ ___ ___ aged

8. si ___ ___ ed

9. ___ ___ ___ ___ ___ eling

10. perm ___ ___ ___ ___ ___ ___

11. l ___ ___ ___ ___ ed

12. rev ___ ___ ing

13. u ___ ___ ___ ___ ed

14. g ___ ___ ___ ___ ___ ___ ing

15. a ___ ___ ___ ___ ed

16. r ___ ___ ___ ___ ___ ed

17. ___ ___ ___ veled

18. cr ___ ___ ___ ___ ___ ___

19. pa___ ___ ___ ___ ___ ing

20. ___ ___ ___ ___ ling

Write the Words

Use the lines below to practice writing the spelling words.

_____ _____ _____ _____

_____ _____ _____ _____

_____ _____ _____ _____

_____ _____ _____ _____

_____ _____ _____ _____

© Macmillan/McGraw-Hill

At Home: Review the Word Study Steps to help the student
spell new words.

Name_____

sloped	stifling	marveled	sipped	encouraged
permitting	orbiting	credited	labored	patrolling
referred	regretting	totaled	unraveling	uttered
reviving	glimmering	accused	confiding	hovered

Write the spelling words with each of the spelling patterns below.

Drop the final *e*

1. _____
2. _____
3. _____

Double the final consonant

4. _____
5. _____
6. _____
7. _____
8. _____

Dropping *-ing* or *-ed*

9. _____
10. _____
11. _____
12. _____
13. _____
14. _____
15. _____
16. _____
17. _____
18. _____

Write About It

Use one of the sets of words above in a short piece of writing about a topic of your choice.

_____

_____

_____

_____

_____

_____

Name_____

sloped	stifling	marveled	sipped	encouraged
permitting	orbiting	credited	labored	patrolling
referred	regretting	totaled	unraveling	uttered
reviving	glimmering	accused	confiding	hovered

Synonyms

Write the spelling word that matches each synonym.

1. approved _____

2. apologizing _____

3. spoken _____

4. allowing _____

5. summed _____

6. wonder _____

Antonyms

Write the spelling word that matches each antonym.

7. praised _____

8. easy _____

9. dejected _____

10. sunk _____

11. destroyed _____

12. guzzle _____

Name_____

Proofreading Activity

As I sat in the park and siped my lemonade, I marvelled at what a beautifully clear day it was. The sky was blue and flawless. Then all of a sudden, out of nowhere, a small glimmerring disc came orbitting out of the sky and hoverd above my head before plummeting to the ground. I sat there amazed for a minute, as the disc came to a halt by my feet. Had I just come into contact with something from another planet? Slightly afraid, I looked down at my feet, only to discover that what I had seen was just your average frisbee.

1. _____
2. _____
3. _____
4. _____
5. _____

Writing Activity

Did you ever think about the possibility of life on other planets? Write a letter to an alien explaining your life on Earth. Use five spelling words.

_____
_____
_____
_____
_____
_____
_____
_____

Name_____

Look at the words in each set below. One word in each set is spelled correctly. Use a pencil to fill in the circle next to the correct word. Before you begin, look at the sample set of words. Sample A has been done for you. Do Sample B by yourself. When you are sure you know what to do, you may go on with the rest of the page.

Sample A:

Ⓐ travelling
Ⓑ travilling
Ⓒ traveling
Ⓓ travelin

Sample B:

Ⓔ tiped
Ⓕ tieped
Ⓖ tipped
Ⓗ tippd

1. Ⓐ slopped
   Ⓑ slopd
   Ⓒ clopped
   Ⓓ sloped

2. Ⓔ encouraged
   Ⓕ incourages
   Ⓖ enncouraged
   Ⓗ encourjd

3. Ⓐ laburd
   Ⓑ labored
   Ⓒ laborred
   Ⓓ labord

4. Ⓔ glimerin
   Ⓕ glimmering
   Ⓖ glimering
   Ⓗ glimaring

5. Ⓐ total
   Ⓑ totuled
   Ⓒ totaled
   Ⓓ totalled

6. Ⓔ stiflign
   Ⓕ stiffling
   Ⓖ stiflinng
   Ⓗ stifling

7. Ⓐ permiting
   Ⓑ prmitting
   Ⓒ pirmitting
   Ⓓ permitting

8. Ⓔ putroling
   Ⓕ patroling
   Ⓖ patrolling
   Ⓗ patrollin

9. Ⓐ accused
   Ⓑ akused
   Ⓒ accussed
   Ⓓ acused

10. Ⓔ unraveling
    Ⓕ unravveling
    Ⓖ unravelling
    Ⓗ unravling

11. Ⓐ marveled
    Ⓑ maveled
    Ⓒ marrveld
    Ⓓ marvld

12. Ⓔ orbitting
    Ⓕ orbiting
    Ⓖ orbittin
    Ⓗ orbtng

13. Ⓐ referd
    Ⓑ referred
    Ⓒ reffered
    Ⓓ reffird

14. Ⓔ confidin
    Ⓕ confiding
    Ⓖ conffiding
    Ⓗ konfiding

15. Ⓐ utered
    Ⓑ utterred
    Ⓒ utterd
    Ⓓ uttered

16. Ⓔ siped
    Ⓕ sippde
    Ⓖ sipped
    Ⓗ sipd

17. Ⓐ creadeted
    Ⓑ creddited
    Ⓒ kredited
    Ⓓ credited

18. Ⓔ regreting
    Ⓕ regrettin
    Ⓖ regretting
    Ⓗ regritteng

19. Ⓐ havered
    Ⓑ hoverred
    Ⓒ hovered
    Ⓓ hoverd

20. Ⓔ raving
    Ⓕ reviving
    Ⓖ revivving
    Ⓗ reving

Name_____

Fold back the paper along the dotted line. Write the words in the blanks as they are read aloud. When you finish the test, unfold the paper. Use the list at the right to correct any spelling mistakes.

1. _____   **1.** vault

2. _____   **2.** slouch

3. _____   **3.** poise

4. _____   **4.** scrawl

5. _____   **5.** noodle

6. _____   **6.** blouse

7. _____   **7.** boost

8. _____   **8.** sooty

9. _____   **9.** fraud

10. _____   **10.** sought

11. _____   **11.** scowl

12. _____   **12.** employ

13. _____   **13.** thaw

14. _____   **14.** groove

15. _____   **15.** corduroy

16. _____   **16.** browse

17. _____   **17.** rookie

18. _____   **18.** scoot

19. _____   **19.** avoid

20. _____   **20.** snoozed

Review Words 21. _____   **21.** sipped

22. _____   **22.** credited

23. _____   **23.** regretting

Challenge Words 24. _____   **24.** drowsy

25. _____   **25.** boisterous

At Home: Help the student practice the words he or she missed to prepare for the Posttest.

© Macmillan/McGraw-Hill

Name_____

Using the Word Study Steps

1. LOOK at the word.

2. SAY the word aloud.

3. STUDY the letters in the word.

4. WRITE the word.

5. CHECK the word.
   Did you spell the word right?
   If not, go back to step 1.

Word Scramble

Unscramble each set of letters to make a spelling word.

1. lwarcs _____

2. otbso _____

3. divao _____

4. stoyo _____

5. wosreb _____

6. talvu _____

7. oolend _____

8. plemoy _____

9. dezosno _____

10. voroge _____

11. gutohs _____

12. twah _____

13. lowsc _____

14. orkoie _____

15. rrooducy _____

16. tosoc _____

17. obules _____

18. daruf _____

19. hlucos _____

20. eiops _____

Write the Words

Use the lines below to practice writing the spelling words.

_____ _____ _____ _____

_____ _____ _____ _____

_____ _____ _____ _____

_____ _____ _____ _____

_____ _____ _____ _____

At Home: Review the Word Study Steps to help the student spell new words.

© Macmillan/McGraw-Hill

Name _____

vault	slouch	poise	scrawl	noodle
blouse	boost	sooty	fraud	sought
scowl	employ	thaw	groove	corduroy
browse	rookie	scoot	avoid	snoozed

Write the spelling words with each of the spelling patterns below.

-au

1. _____
2. _____

-ou

3. _____
4. _____
5. _____

-oi

6. _____
7. _____

-aw

8. _____
9. _____

-oo

10. _____
11. _____
12. _____
13. _____
14. _____
15. _____
16. _____

-ow

17. _____
18. _____

-oy

19. _____
20. _____

vault	slouch	poise	scrawl	noodle
blouse	boost	sooty	fraud	sought
scowl	employ	thaw	groove	corduroy
browse	rookie	scoot	avoid	snoozed

Sentence Completion

Fill in the blank with the appropriate spelling word.

1. My sister's overalls are made out of blue _____.

2. We had to let the frozen meat _____ before we cooked it.

3. My mother says I must always sit up straight, as it is impolite to

   _____.

4. When they discovered the hidden _____, they found the stolen jewels.

5. After a long day at the beach, we came home and _____.

6. The ice cream cone dripped all over my new _____.

7. I like to _____ through the new releases at the music store.

8. The restaurant is looking to _____ a new chef.

9. Before I leave I _____ the address of where I am going on a piece of paper.

10. The best new athlete wins the _____ of the year award.

11. After getting in trouble at school, Shawna wore a _____ on her face.

12. I couldn't see over the counter so I asked for a _____.

13. The walls of the old building were very _____ from all the candles.

14. My father walked to the podium with great grace and _____.

15. The museum officials were relieved to discover that the masterpiece was

    not a _____.

16. Mayank was happy to find his lucky pencil stuck in a _____.

Name_____

Proofreading Activity

When The Noodal House first opened, I thought it might be a nice place to work. I applied for a job and they agreed to imploy me. Because I was the last person they hired, they called me "rooky" and teased me a lot for not knowing how to do everything. After a week, I began to go to work with a scowel on my face. This is not the type of work environment that I had sawt.

1. _____

2. _____

3. _____

4. _____

5. _____

Writing Activity

Did you ever have a job? Write about a job you have had, or would like to have someday. Use five spelling words.

_____

_____

_____

_____

_____

_____

_____

_____

_____

Name_____

Look at the words in each set below. One word in each set is
spelled correctly. Use a pencil to fill in the circle next to the correct
word. Before you begin, look at the sample set of words. Sample
A has been done for you. Do Sample B by yourself. When you are
sure you know what to do, you may go on with the rest of the page.

Sample A:

Ⓐ powch
Ⓑ pooch
Ⓒ pouch
Ⓓ puoch

Sample B:

Ⓔ mowse
Ⓕ mose
Ⓖ mouse
Ⓗ muose

1. Ⓐ valt
   Ⓑ vualt
   Ⓒ vault
   Ⓓ vautl

2. Ⓔ noodle
   Ⓕ knewdle
   Ⓖ nodel
   Ⓗ newdle

3. Ⓐ frawd
   Ⓑ fraud
   Ⓒ fruad
   Ⓓ frad

4. Ⓔ thaw
   Ⓕ thuw
   Ⓖ thoow
   Ⓗ thaaw

5. Ⓐ roockee
   Ⓑ rooike
   Ⓒ rokie
   Ⓓ rookie

6. Ⓔ clouch
   Ⓕ slouch
   Ⓖ slooch
   Ⓗ sluoch

7. Ⓐ bluse
   Ⓑ blowse
   Ⓒ bluse
   Ⓓ blouse

8. Ⓔ sought
   Ⓕ suot
   Ⓖ sout
   Ⓗ soght

9. Ⓐ grove
   Ⓑ groov
   Ⓒ groove
   Ⓓ grooev

10. Ⓔ scoot
    Ⓕ soot
    Ⓖ scott
    Ⓗ scewt

11. Ⓐ poose
    Ⓑ poise
    Ⓒ posie
    Ⓓ piose

12. Ⓔ bost
    Ⓕ boots
    Ⓖ boost
    Ⓗ bewst

13. Ⓐ cowl
    Ⓑ scoll
    Ⓒ scwol
    Ⓓ scowl

14. Ⓔ korduory
    Ⓕ corduroy
    Ⓖ cordroy
    Ⓗ cordouroy

15. Ⓐ afoid
    Ⓑ avoid
    Ⓒ avowd
    Ⓓ avood

16. Ⓔ skrawl
    Ⓕ scrarawl
    Ⓖ scrowl
    Ⓗ scrawl

17. Ⓐ sewty
    Ⓑ soty
    Ⓒ sooty
    Ⓓ soote

18. Ⓔ imploy
    Ⓕ emply
    Ⓖ empoly
    Ⓗ employ

19. Ⓐ brawse
    Ⓑ browse
    Ⓒ browes
    Ⓓ brose

20. Ⓔ snoized
    Ⓕ snewzed
    Ⓖ snoozed
    Ⓗ snozed

© Macmillan/McGraw-Hill

Name_____

Fold back the paper along the dotted line. Write the words in the blanks as they are read aloud. When you finish the test, unfold the paper. Use the list at the right to correct any spelling mistakes.

1. _____
2. _____
3. _____
4. _____
5. _____
6. _____
7. _____
8. _____
9. _____
10. _____
11. _____
12. _____
13. _____
14. _____
15. _____
16. _____
17. _____
18. _____
19. _____
20. _____

Review Words 21. _____
22. _____
23. _____

Challenge Words 24. _____
25. _____

1. factor
2. banner
3. victim
4. mental
5. formal
6. pantry
7. ballot
8. prosper
9. pumpkin
10. muffler
11. ragged
12. kingdom
13. barren
14. necklace
15. wallet
16. ponder
17. funnel
18. dwelling
19. snapshot
20. fabric
21. blouse
22. employ
23. thaw
24. verdict
25. garment

At Home: Help the student practice the words he or she missed to prepare for the Posttest.

Name_____

Using the Word Study Steps

1. LOOK at the word.

2. SAY the word aloud.

3. STUDY the letters in the word.

4. WRITE the word.

5. CHECK the word.
   Did you spell the word right?
   If not, go back to step 1.

Find Rhyming Words

Circle the word in each row that rhymes with the spelling word on the left.

1. **mental**	lintel	gentle	mindless
2. **dwelling**	rebel	climbing	swelling
3. **snapshot**	plot	blank	cap
4. **ponder**	winner	wander	wonder
5. **pumpkin**	bumpkin	stumped	flint
6. **funnel**	run	tunnel	camel
7. **factor**	tractor	lecture	alligator
8. **banner**	runner	junior	manor
9. **necklace**	glass	reckless	trace
10. **ballot**	bullet	slot	palette

Write a poem of at least 4 lines. Include two of the spelling words in your poem.

_____

_____

_____

_____

© Macmillan/McGraw-Hill

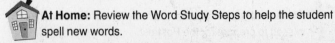 **At Home:** Review the Word Study Steps to help the student spell new words.

Name_____

factor	banner	victim	mental	formal
pantry	ballot	prosper	pumpkin	muffler
ragged	kingdom	barren	necklace	wallet
ponder	funnel	dwelling	snapshot	fabric

Write the spelling words with each of the spelling patterns below.

VCCV

1. _____
2. _____
3. _____
4. _____
5. _____
6. _____
7. _____
8. _____
9. _____
10. _____
11. _____
12. _____
13. _____
14. _____

VCCCV

15. _____
16. _____
17. _____
18. _____
19. _____
20. _____

Alphabetical Order
Use the lines below to write the spelling words in alphabetical order.

_____ _____ _____ _____

_____ _____ _____ _____

_____ _____ _____ _____

_____ _____ _____ _____

_____

Name_____

factor	banner	victim	mental	formal
pantry	ballot	prosper	pumpkin	muffler
ragged	kingdom	barren	necklace	wallet
ponder	funnel	dwelling	snapshot	fabric

Matching Meanings

Write the spelling word that matches each definition.

1. poster _____

2. infertile _____

3. consider _____

4. cloth _____

5. sufferer _____

6. cupboard _____

7. house _____

8. vote _____

9. kingdom _____

10. photograph _____

11. uneven _____

12. successful _____

13. proper _____

14. scarf _____

15. country _____

16. aparatus _____

Name_____

Proofreading Activity

Last year, I started a small detective business in my town. When a crime occurs people come to me to try to solve it. I have yet to have a case go unsolved. Today, around 4:30 p.m., my friend Jahlani Philips came to me. He said that his mother had been on her way to her friend's house last night for dinner when she noticed that the neckless she intended to wear was missing.

I immediately followed him to his house to interview the viktim. Once there I asked her if she had any pictures of the stolen goods. She handed us a snapposht of the diamond jewelry. I then asked Jahlani's mother to recall her activities from yesterday. She explained that she had been wearing the jewelry all day, but took it off in the afternoon while she was making a pumcken pie for the dinner party. When she went to put it back on, she realized it had been stolen.

"Where did you take off your jewelry?" I asked.

"Why in my bedroom, of course, and I placed it back into my jewelry box just like I always do. When I returned to get it for the party, it was gone."

"Do you mind if I have a look around?" I asked, heading for the kitchen.

"Not at all," she replied.

First, I checked the refrigerator, which did not contain the stolen goods. But upon opening the door to the pantree, I uncovered the missing property. Jahlani's mother was so happy with my discovery, she gave me a hug.

1. _____ 2. _____ 3. _____

4. _____ 5. _____

Writing Activity

Have you ever lost something important to you? Write about a time when you thought you had lost an important object and how you felt when you found it. Use five spelling words.

_____

_____

_____

_____

Name_____

Look at the words in each set below. One word in each set is spelled correctly. Use a pencil to fill in the circle next to the correct word. Before you begin, look at the sample set of words. Sample A has been done for you. Do Sample B by yourself. When you are sure you know what to do, you may go on with the rest of the page.

Sample A:

Ⓐ maner
Ⓑ mannir
Ⓒ manner
Ⓓ mannr

Sample B:

Ⓔ tunel
Ⓕ tunnil
Ⓖ tunnel
Ⓗ tunell

1. Ⓐ faktor
   Ⓑ facter
   Ⓒ factor
   Ⓓ factr

2. Ⓔ barren
   Ⓕ barrin
   Ⓖ barrn
   Ⓗ barrne

3. Ⓐ ragged
   Ⓑ raged
   Ⓒ ragid
   Ⓓ raggde

4. Ⓔ pantree
   Ⓕ pantri
   Ⓖ pantry
   Ⓗ patnyr

5. Ⓐ balit
   Ⓑ ballit
   Ⓒ balot
   Ⓓ ballot

6. Ⓔ necklace
   Ⓕ neclace
   Ⓖ neklace
   Ⓗ necklaec

7. Ⓐ banr
   Ⓑ banner
   Ⓒ bannir
   Ⓓ baner

8. Ⓔ cingdom
   Ⓕ kingdum
   Ⓖ kingdm
   Ⓗ kingdom

9. Ⓐ funil
   Ⓑ funnel
   Ⓒ funel
   Ⓓ funnle

10. Ⓔ snapshot
    Ⓕ snapsot
    Ⓖ cnapshot
    Ⓗ snapshott

11. Ⓐ viktum
    Ⓑ victim
    Ⓒ victum
    Ⓓ victm

12. Ⓔ wallit
    Ⓕ walet
    Ⓖ wallt
    Ⓗ wallet

13. Ⓐ firml
    Ⓑ forml
    Ⓒ formal
    Ⓓ formil

14. Ⓔ fabrec
    Ⓕ fabrik
    Ⓖ fabric
    Ⓗ fabrc

15. Ⓐ prosper
    Ⓑ prospir
    Ⓒ prospr
    Ⓓ prossper

16. Ⓔ mentale
    Ⓕ mentl
    Ⓖ mentul
    Ⓗ mental

17. Ⓐ mufler
    Ⓑ muffler
    Ⓒ mufflir
    Ⓓ mufflr

18. Ⓔ ponder
    Ⓕ pondir
    Ⓖ pondr
    Ⓗ pondre

19. Ⓐ dwellin
    Ⓑ dwellen
    Ⓒ dwelling
    Ⓓ dwellng

20. Ⓔ pumcin
    Ⓕ pumkin
    Ⓖ pumpkin
    Ⓗ pumpkine

Name_____

Fold back the paper along the dotted line. Write the words in the blanks as they are read aloud. When you finish the test, unfold the paper. Use the list at the right to correct any spelling mistakes.

1. _____
2. _____
3. _____
4. _____
5. _____
6. _____
7. _____
8. _____
9. _____
10. _____
11. _____
12. _____
13. _____
14. _____
15. _____
16. _____
17. _____
18. _____
19. _____
20. _____

Review Words 21. _____

22. _____

23. _____

Challenge Words 24. _____

25. _____

1. brutal
2. secure
3. panic
4. cabins
5. fever
6. voter
7. vanish
8. nylon
9. detect
10. resist
11. labor
12. focus
13. rival
14. recite
15. topic
16. amid
17. unit
18. rotate
19. vital
20. lament
21. victim
22. wallet
23. snapshot
24. mural
25. civic

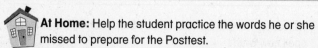

At Home: Help the student practice the words he or she missed to prepare for the Posttest.

Name_____

Using the Word Study Steps

1. LOOK at the word.

2. SAY the word aloud.

3. STUDY the letters in the word.

4. WRITE the word.

5. CHECK the word.
   Did you spell the word right?
   If not, go back to step 1.

Write the spelling words in alphabetical order.

1. _____   11. _____

2. _____   12. _____

3. _____   13. _____

4. _____   14. _____

5. _____   15. _____

6. _____   16. _____

7. _____   17. _____

8. _____   18. _____

9. _____   19. _____

10. _____   20. _____

Write the Words

Use the lines below to practice writing the spelling words.

_____   _____   _____   _____

_____   _____   _____   _____

_____   _____   _____   _____

_____   _____   _____   _____

_____   _____   _____   _____

© Macmillan/McGraw-Hill

At Home: Review the Word Study Steps to help the student spell new words.

Name

brutal	secure	panic	cabins	fever
voter	vanish	nylon	detect	resist
focus	rival	recite	topic	amid
unit	rotate	vital	lament	withdraw

Crossword Puzzle

Use the clues to complete the puzzle.

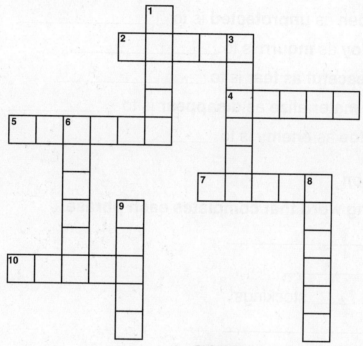

ACROSS

2. At eighteen it is important to become a _____.

4. My paper _____ is the Civil War.

5. When we went camping we stayed in _____.

7. She was sick with a high _____.

10. My costume was made with _____ and feathers.

DOWN

1. When I am bored, I find it difficult to _____.

3. We _____ activities during gym class.

6. War is often extremely _____.

8. I have to _____ my poem at the fair.

9. Before the exam, I began to _____.

Name_____

brutal	secure	panic	cabins	fever
voter	vanish	nylon	detect	resist
focus	rival	recite	topic	amid
unit	rotate	vital	lament	withdraw

Analogies

Complete each analogy with the appropriate spelling word.

1. **Lock** is to **open** as **unprotected** is to _____.

2. **Happy** is to **joy** as **mourn** is to _____.

3. **Calm** is to **peaceful** as **fear** is to _____.

4. **Appear** is to **materialize** as **disappear** is to _____.

5. **Friend** is to **foe** as **enemy** is to _____.

Phrase Completion

Write the spelling word that completes each phrase.

6. registered _____

7. log _____

8. _____ stockings

9. term paper _____

10. low grade _____

More Analogies

Write some analogies of your own on the lines below. Use at least one spelling word in each analogy.

11. _____

12. _____

Proofreading Activity

Last year, before my brother went off to college, my family took a vacation to Maine for a week. We stayed in cabends umid the trees and tried to forus on just spending time together. Though I still see my brother all the time, I can't ressist thinking that our vacation last summer will remain a vitale memory for me.

1. _____   2. _____   3. _____

4. _____   5. _____

Writing Activity

Have you ever had to say goodbye to a good friend or family member when they moved away? Write a description of what it was like for them to leave. Use at least five spelling words.

_____

_____

_____

_____

_____

_____

_____

_____

_____

_____

_____

_____

_____

Look at the words in each set below. One word in each set is spelled correctly. Use a pencil to fill in the circle next to the correct word. Before you begin, look at the sample set of words. Sample A has been done for you. Do Sample B by yourself. When you are sure you know what to do, you may go on with the rest of the page.

Sample A:

Ⓐ nevr
Ⓑ nevre
Ⓒ never
Ⓓ nevir

Sample B:

Ⓔ banesh
Ⓕ bannish
Ⓖ banish
Ⓗ banush

1. Ⓐ brutil
Ⓑ burtal
Ⓒ brutal
Ⓓ brutl

2. Ⓔ nilon
Ⓕ nylonn
Ⓖ nylon
Ⓗ nyln

3. Ⓐ datect
Ⓑ ditect
Ⓒ dettect
Ⓓ detect

4. Ⓔ rotat
Ⓕ rotatee
Ⓖ rotate
Ⓗ rotatte

5. Ⓐ votur
Ⓑ votir
Ⓒ votr
Ⓓ voter

6. Ⓔ lament
Ⓕ lamen
Ⓖ lument
Ⓗ lametn

7. Ⓐ resist
Ⓑ resest
Ⓒ ressist
Ⓓ resit

8. Ⓔ cabuns
Ⓕ cabins
Ⓖ cabenns
Ⓗ cabinns

9. Ⓐ topic
Ⓑ topec
Ⓒ topac
Ⓓ topick

10. Ⓔ resite
Ⓕ recite
Ⓖ recit
Ⓗ recitte

11. Ⓐ cecure
Ⓑ secre
Ⓒ secure
Ⓓ secrue

12. Ⓔ panec
Ⓕ pannic
Ⓖ panc
Ⓗ panic

13. Ⓐ unit
Ⓑ unet
Ⓒ unite
Ⓓ unitt

14. Ⓔ fevur
Ⓕ fevor
Ⓖ fever
Ⓗ fervar

15. Ⓐ revel
Ⓑ rivalle
Ⓒ rivul
Ⓓ rival

16. Ⓔ vital
Ⓕ vitil
Ⓖ vitl
Ⓗ vitale

17. Ⓐ vanish
Ⓑ vanush
Ⓒ vanesh
Ⓓ vanich

18. Ⓔ labur
Ⓕ labr
Ⓖ labor
Ⓗ laberr

19. Ⓐ fokus
Ⓑ fockus
Ⓒ focis
Ⓓ focus

20. Ⓔ emid
Ⓕ ammid
Ⓖ amed
Ⓗ amid

© Macmillan/McGraw-Hill

Name_____

Read each sentence. If an underlined word is spelled wrong, fill in the circle that goes with that word. If no word is spelled wrong, fill in the circle below NONE. Read Sample A, and do Sample B.

A. On the <u>shelves</u> were <u>book's</u> about <u>wolves</u> and <u>buffalos</u>.
          A   B   C

                            NONE
A. Ⓐ Ⓑ ⬤ Ⓓ

B. As the <u>thieves</u> cracked opened the <u>valt</u>, they were caught
            E   F

by the <u>sheriffs</u>.
      G

                            NONE
B. Ⓔ Ⓕ Ⓖ Ⓗ

1. My aunt thinks that the fit of your <u>blowse</u> can determine if
                                  A

you <u>slouch</u> or stand with <u>poise</u>.
     B   C

                            NONE
1. Ⓐ Ⓑ Ⓒ Ⓓ

2. I had to <u>browse</u> through piles of <u>sooty</u> things at the yard
            E   F

sale to find the <u>necklace</u>.
          G

                            NONE
2. Ⓔ Ⓕ Ⓖ Ⓗ

3. She had a <u>fever</u>, she <u>snoozd</u>, and did not leave her <u>dwelling</u>.
          A   B   C

                            NONE
3. Ⓐ Ⓑ Ⓒ Ⓓ

4. After his <u>wallet</u> was stolen, Jason became the <u>victim</u> of identity
           E   F

<u>frawd</u>.
  G

                            NONE
4. Ⓔ Ⓕ Ⓖ Ⓗ

5. As part of the student elections, I <u>encouraged</u> <u>voter</u> turnout
                                 A   B

and was a <u>ballot</u> counter.
          C

                            NONE
5. Ⓐ Ⓑ Ⓒ Ⓓ

6. We <u>marveled</u> at the <u>glimmerring</u> <u>photos</u>.
          E   F   G

                            NONE
6. Ⓔ Ⓕ Ⓖ Ⓗ

7. Listening to the <u>wives</u> speak, it was hard to believe the
                    A

<u>datta</u> that was <u>uttered</u>.
   B   C

                            NONE
7. Ⓐ Ⓑ Ⓒ Ⓓ

8. The chef <u>hovered</u> over his <u>loaves</u> of bread as though it were
           E   F

a <u>kingdom</u>.
    G

                            NONE
8. Ⓔ Ⓕ Ⓖ Ⓗ

Name_____

9. The <u>rookie</u> cop was nervously <u>patroling</u> the area, every so often
     A   B

   pulling at his <u>cuffs</u> and jacket.
                    C

9. Ⓐ Ⓑ Ⓒ Ⓓ NONE

10. I sought <u>cordoroy</u> <u>scarves</u> to buy for all my friends.
       E   F   G

10. Ⓔ Ⓕ Ⓖ Ⓗ NONE

11. In the <u>pantry</u> were all the ingredients for my famous <u>pumpkin</u>
            A   B

   <u>noodle</u> pudding.
     C

11. Ⓐ Ⓑ Ⓒ Ⓓ NONE

12. During <u>tornados</u> log <u>cabins</u> fall down like <u>dominoes</u>.
              E   F   G

12. Ⓔ Ⓕ Ⓖ Ⓗ NONE

13. When I feel <u>sekure</u>, I know nothing <u>brutal</u> will happen and I do
                  A   B

   not <u>panic</u>.
        C

13. Ⓐ Ⓑ Ⓒ Ⓓ NONE

14. It is illegal to <u>resist</u> arrest or <u>avoid</u> the police when you are
                      E   F

   <u>accussed</u> of a crime.
     G

14. Ⓔ Ⓕ Ⓖ Ⓗ NONE

15. He was <u>regreting</u> <u>confiding</u> in the <u>media</u>.
              A   B   C

15. Ⓐ Ⓑ Ⓒ Ⓓ NONE

16. The unit of <u>sopranoes</u> created powerful <u>echoes</u>.
       E   F   G

16. Ⓔ Ⓕ Ⓖ Ⓗ NONE

17. After the snowstorm, the <u>muffler</u> needed to <u>thaw</u> and the car
                              A   B

   needed a <u>booste</u>.
               C

17. Ⓐ Ⓑ Ⓒ Ⓓ NONE

18. <u>Nylon</u> <u>fabric</u> was <u>vital</u> for the costumes we made for the play.
      E   F   G

18. Ⓔ Ⓕ Ⓖ Ⓗ NONE

19. My <u>topic</u> was to <u>focus</u> on underwater <u>volcanose</u>.
          A   B   C

19. Ⓐ Ⓑ Ⓒ Ⓓ NONE

20. For the sixth grade party everyone had to <u>scrawl</u> their name
                                                E

   on a <u>banner</u>, but the pen got stuck in a <u>groove</u> in the floor.
          F   G

20. Ⓔ Ⓕ Ⓖ Ⓗ NONE

Name_____

Fold back the paper along the dotted line. Write the words in the blanks as they are read aloud. When you finish the test, unfold the paper. Use the list at the right to correct any spelling mistakes.

1. _____
2. _____
3. _____
4. _____
5. _____
6. _____
7. _____
8. _____
9. _____
10. _____
11. _____
12. _____
13. _____
14. _____
15. _____
16. _____
17. _____
18. _____
19. _____
20. _____

Review Words 21. _____
22. _____
23. _____

Challenge Words 24. _____
25. _____

1. ignore
2. wealthy
3. fulfill
4. healthy
5. enroll
6. accept
7. parchment
8. dismay
9. debate
10. prepare
11. repair
12. applaud
13. forlorn
14. shoulder
15. abroad
16. flounder
17. saunter
18. falter
19. install
20. bounty
21. voter
22. recite
23. topic
24. jaunty
25. cauldron

© Macmillan/McGraw-Hill

At Home: Help the student practice the words he or she missed to prepare for the Posttest.

Name_____

Using the Word Study Steps

1. LOOK at the word.

2. SAY the word aloud.

3. STUDY the letters in the word.

4. WRITE the word.

5. CHECK the word.
   Did you spell the word right?
   If not, go back to step 1.

Missing Letters

Fill in the missing letters to form spelling words.

1. fl _____ er

2. parch _____

3. heal _____ y

4. _____ roll

5. bo _____ y

6. f _____ er

7. _____ pare

8. fo _____ rn

9. we _____ y

10. in _____

11. ful _____

12. de _____ e

13. _____ laud

14. i _____ ore

15. saun _____ r

16. _____ may

17. a _____ pt

18. _____ broad

19. sh _____ lder

20. re _____ r

Write the Words

Use the lines to practice writing the spelling words.

_____ _____ _____ _____

_____ _____ _____ _____

_____ _____ _____ _____

_____ _____ _____ _____

_____ _____ _____ _____

At Home: Review the Word Study Steps to help the student spell new words.

© Macmillan/McGraw-Hill

ignore	wealthy	fulfill	healthy	enroll
accept	parchment	dismay	debate	prepare
repair	applaud	forlorn	shoulder	abroad
flounder	saunter	falter	install	bounty

Sort each spelling word by the accented syllable.

First syllable

1. _____
2. _____
3. _____
4. _____
5. _____
6. _____
7. _____
8. _____

Second syllable

9. _____
10. _____
11. _____
12. _____
13. _____
14. _____
15. _____
16. _____
17. _____
18. _____
19. _____
20. _____

Alphabetical Order

Use the lines below to write the spelling words in alphabetical order.

_____ _____ _____ _____ _____

_____ _____ _____ _____ _____

_____ _____ _____ _____ _____

_____ _____ _____ _____ _____

notice	wealthy	fulfill	healthy	enroll
accept	parchment	dismay	debate	prepare
repair	applaud	forlorn	shoulder	abroad
flounder	saunter	falter	install	bounty

Synonyms

Write the spelling word that matches each synonym.

1. argue _____

2. mend _____

3. rich _____

4. register _____

5. stroll _____

6. stumble _____

Antonyms

Write the spelling word that matches each antonym.

7. boo _____

8. penalty _____

9. notice _____

10. ill _____

11. deny _____

12. demolish _____

Use the Spelling Words

**Write two sentences on the lines below. Use a spelling word in
each sentence.**

13. _____

14. _____

Name

Proofreading Activity

There are five spelling mistakes in the paragraph below. Circle the misspelled words. Write the words correctly on the lines below.

When Juan Verdades met Araceli he could not ignor the beauty and charm of the young girl. He wanted to marry her but felt the girl would not marry a man who was not wellthy enough to fulfil her every dream. However, Juan could not change who he was. Even when tested, his true nature could not faulter. In the end Juan stayed true to his truthful nature and was greatly rewarded. Araceli was able to see that he was just as good as he said he was, and acepted him just the way he was.

1. _____   3. _____   5. _____

2. _____   4. _____

Writing Activity

Think of a time when you felt like someone was testing your character to see if you would change under pressure. Write a short paragraph explaining what happened and whether or not you stayed as true to yourself as Juan Verdades. Use five spelling words.

_____

_____

_____

_____

_____

_____

_____

_____

Name_____

Look at the words in each set below. One word in each set is
spelled correctly. Use a pencil to fill in the circle next to the correct
word. Before you begin, look at the sample set of words. Sample
A has been done for you. Do Sample B by yourself. When you are
sure you know what to do, you may go on with the rest of the page.

Sample A:

Ⓐ ribate
Ⓑ rebat
Ⓒ rebate
Ⓓ reebate

Sample B:

Ⓔ boldir
Ⓕ boldr
Ⓖ bolder
Ⓗ bowlder

1. Ⓐ egnor
   Ⓑ ignre
   Ⓒ ignore
   Ⓓ ignoer

2. Ⓔ fullfill
   Ⓕ fulfil
   Ⓖ fullfel
   Ⓗ fulfill

3. Ⓐ healthy
   Ⓑ helthy
   Ⓒ healty
   Ⓓ healthe

4. Ⓔ acept
   Ⓕ accept
   Ⓖ akecept
   Ⓗ acceptt

5. Ⓐ bountee
   Ⓑ bownty
   Ⓒ bounty
   Ⓓ bountey

6. Ⓔ aplowd
   Ⓕ applaud
   Ⓖ aplaud
   Ⓗ appluad

7. Ⓐ flounder
   Ⓑ flownder
   Ⓒ founder
   Ⓓ floudr

8. Ⓔ inroll
   Ⓕ enrol
   Ⓖ enroll
   Ⓗ enrell

9. Ⓐ parcment
   Ⓑ parchmint
   Ⓒ parchmunt
   Ⓓ parchment

10. Ⓔ abroad
    Ⓕ abrod
    Ⓖ abrad
    Ⓗ abrood

11. Ⓐ dismay
    Ⓑ dissmay
    Ⓒ desmay
    Ⓓ dismae

12. Ⓔ sawnter
    Ⓕ sauntr
    Ⓖ saunter
    Ⓗ sauntir

13. Ⓐ prepair
    Ⓑ prepar
    Ⓒ pripare
    Ⓓ prepare

14. Ⓔ install
    Ⓕ enstall
    Ⓖ enstal
    Ⓗ instal

15. Ⓐ sholder
    Ⓑ shoulder
    Ⓒ sholdr
    Ⓓ shouldr

16. Ⓔ wellthy
    Ⓕ wealthe
    Ⓖ wealthy
    Ⓗ waelthe

17. Ⓐ fourlon
    Ⓑ forlorn
    Ⓒ forlon
    Ⓓ fourlorn

18. Ⓔ dibate
    Ⓕ debate
    Ⓖ debeight
    Ⓗ debte

19. Ⓐ fallter
    Ⓑ faltre
    Ⓒ falter
    Ⓓ flatir

20. Ⓔ repair
    Ⓕ repare
    Ⓖ ripari
    Ⓗ repar

© Macmillan/McGraw-Hill

Name_____

Fold back the paper along the dotted line. Write the words in the blanks as they are read aloud. When you finish the test, unfold the paper. Use the list at the right to correct any spelling mistakes.

1. _____ 1. actor
2. _____ 2. stroller
3. _____ 3. scatter
4. _____ 4. gutter
5. _____ 5. platter
6. _____ 6. customer
7. _____ 7. ancestor
8. _____ 8. flavor
9. _____ 9. mirror
10. _____ 10. vinegar
11. _____ 11. bachelor
12. _____ 12. behavior
13. _____ 13. calendar
14. _____ 14. waiter
15. _____ 15. singular
16. _____ 16. maneuver
17. _____ 17. observer
18. _____ 18. wander
19. _____ 19. traitor
20. _____ 20. janitor

Review Words 21. _____ 21. healthy
22. _____ 22. accept
23. _____ 23. prepare

Challenge Words 24. _____ 24. clamor
25. _____ 25. rescuer

© Macmillan/McGraw-Hill

At Home: Help the student practice the words he or she missed to prepare for the Posttest.

Name_____

Using the Word Study Steps

1. LOOK at the word.

2. SAY the word aloud.

3. STUDY the letters in the word.

4. WRITE the word.

5. CHECK the word. Did you spell the word right? If not, go back to step 1.

Crossword Puzzle

Use the clues to complete the puzzle.

ACROSS

1. Eva enjoyed the soup but felt it had too much _____.

6. Mr. Change brought over a _____ of trout.

7. I wish I could play field hockey, but I'm only an _____.

9. Eva liked witnessing the unusual _____ on 90th Street.

10. Being a _____ at the 90th Street Café would be an interesting job.

DOWN

2. When the ball hit the deliveryman, the pizza landed in the _____.

3. Mr. Sims is a great _____ on Broadway.

4. The soup had more _____ when Mrs. Martinez added spices.

5. When the pizza fell the toppings began to _____.

8. Baby Joshua sat in a _____.

At Home: Review the Word Study Steps to help the student spell new words.

Name_____

actor	stroller	scatter	gutter	platter
customer	ancestor	flavor	mirror	vinegar
bachelor	behavior	calendar	waiter	singular
maneuver	observer	wander	traitor	janitor

Place the spelling words in their appropriate column according to their final *schwa-r*.

-ar

1. _____
2. _____
3. _____

-or

4. _____
5. _____
6. _____
7. _____
8. _____
9. _____
10. _____
11. _____

-er

12. _____
13. _____
14. _____
15. _____
16. _____
17. _____
18. _____
19. _____
20. _____

Alphabetical Order

Use the lines below to write the spelling words in alphabetical order.

_____ _____ _____ _____

_____ _____ _____ _____

_____ _____ _____ _____

_____ _____ _____ _____

_____ _____ _____ _____

Name_____

actor	stroller	scatter	gutter	platter
customer	ancestor	flavor	mirror	vinegar
bachelor	behavior	calendar	waiter	singular
maneuver	observer	wander	traitor	janitor

Word Meanings

Write the spelling word that matches each definition.

1. a water drain alongside a road _____

2. referring to one person or thing _____

3. to throw things around _____

4. a disloyal person _____

5. the manner in which one conducts oneself _____

6. a large flat serving dish _____

7. a quality of food or drink detected by the senses _____

8. a skillful movement or action _____

9. buggy _____

10. a buyer of goods or services _____

11. an unmarried man _____

12. member of your family who lived a long time ago _____

13. chart showing days, weeks, months in a year _____

14. surface that reflects the image in front of it _____

15. to get lost; to stray _____

Proofreading Activity

There are five spelling mistakes in the paragraph below. Circle the misspelled words. Write the words correctly on the lines below.

Interesting events happen at the most unlikely of times. Watching the street on a boring day can prove to be one of the most entertaining events. Try to be a careful serobver. You never know who will walk by. The neighborhood ackter may erdanw by rehearsing a monologue. The wayter from the local restaurant may run across the street to the deli to stock up on extra vineger. The daily activities of those in your neighborhood can often be quite unusual and exciting.

1. _____   3. _____   5. _____

2. _____   4. _____

Writing Activity

Think about a time when something unusual happened that you didn't expect. Write a paragraph about that particular day. Use five spelling words.

_____

_____

_____

_____

_____

_____

_____

_____

Name_____

Look at the words in each set below. One word in each set is spelled correctly. Use a pencil to fill in the circle next to the correct word. Before you begin, look at the sample set of words. Sample A has been done for you. Do Sample B by yourself. When you are sure you know what to do, you may go on with the rest of the page.

Sample A:

Ⓐ senator
Ⓑ senater
Ⓒ cenator
Ⓓ senatr

Sample B:

Ⓔ similir
Ⓕ similar
Ⓖ similurr
Ⓗ simillar

1. Ⓐ flavir
   Ⓑ flavor
   Ⓒ flavr
   Ⓓ flavar

2. Ⓔ calinder
   Ⓕ calendar
   Ⓖ calender
   Ⓗ kalendar

3. Ⓐ ancestor
   Ⓑ ancestore
   Ⓒ ancester
   Ⓓ ansecter

4. Ⓔ water
   Ⓕ waitir
   Ⓖ waiter
   Ⓗ waitor

5. Ⓐ mirrer
   Ⓑ mirror
   Ⓒ mirar
   Ⓓ miror

6. Ⓔ custimer
   Ⓕ customer
   Ⓖ customar
   Ⓗ kustomer

7. Ⓐ cinguler
   Ⓑ singulur
   Ⓒ singullir
   Ⓓ singular

8. Ⓔ vineger
   Ⓕ vingr
   Ⓖ vinagar
   Ⓗ vinegar

9. Ⓐ scater
   Ⓑ skattir
   Ⓒ scatter
   Ⓓ skatter

10. Ⓔ abroad
    Ⓕ abrod
    Ⓖ abrad
    Ⓗ abrood

11. Ⓐ bachelor
    Ⓑ bachelir
    Ⓒ bachalor
    Ⓓ bahelor

12. Ⓔ stroler
    Ⓕ strollar
    Ⓖ stroller
    Ⓗ strollr

13. Ⓐ plater
    Ⓑ plattar
    Ⓒ platter
    Ⓓ platir

14. Ⓔ gutter
    Ⓕ guter
    Ⓖ guttir
    Ⓗ gutir

15. Ⓐ traitor
    Ⓑ trator
    Ⓒ traiter
    Ⓓ traittor

16. Ⓔ behavir
    Ⓕ behaveor
    Ⓖ behavor
    Ⓗ behavior

17. Ⓐ janitor
    Ⓑ jantor
    Ⓒ janator
    Ⓓ janiter

18. Ⓔ manewver
    Ⓕ maneuver
    Ⓖ manuver
    Ⓗ manuvere

19. Ⓐ obserrvar
    Ⓑ obsrver
    Ⓒ observir
    Ⓓ observer

20. Ⓔ actir
    Ⓕ aktor
    Ⓖ actor
    Ⓗ actar

Spelling

Final *schwa-n*
and *schwa-l*:
Pretest

Name _____

Fold back the paper along the dotted line. Write the words in the blanks as they are read aloud. When you finish the test, unfold the paper. Use the list at the right to correct any spelling mistakes.

1. _____
2. _____
3. _____
4. _____
5. _____
6. _____
7. _____
8. _____
9. _____
10. _____
11. _____
12. _____
13. _____
14. _____
15. _____
16. _____
17. _____
18. _____
19. _____
20. _____

Review Words 21. _____
22. _____
23. _____

Challenge Words 24. _____
25. _____

1. burden
2. carton
3. hasten
4. cable
5. civil
6. dwindle
7. gallon
8. fumble
9. normal
10. novel
11. basin
12. whistle
13. villain
14. urban
15. organ
16. satin
17. curtain
18. peril
19. gravel
20. dangle
21. customer
22. flavor
23. calendar
24. vertical
25. verteran

© Macmillan/McGraw-Hill

At Home: Help the student practice the words he or she missed to prepare for the Posttest.

Name_____

Using the Word Study Steps

1. LOOK at the word.

2. SAY the word aloud.

3. STUDY the letters in the word.

4. WRITE the word.

5. CHECK the word.
   Did you spell the word right?
   If not, go back to step 1.

Find Rhyming Words

Put an *X* on the one word that rhymes with the spelling word on the left.

1. **dangle**	eagle	angle	angel
2. **cable**	cobble	kettle	table
3. **satin**	latin	saffron	cretin
4. **novel**	grovel	gravel	barrel
5. **carton**	apron	spartan	plankton
6. **dwindle**	thimble	candle	kindle
7. **curtain**	certain	maintain	attain
8. **whistle**	castle	wrestle	missile
9. **gravel**	crave	cradle	travel
10. **normal**	formal	female	thermal
11. **fumble**	stumble	thumb	plum
12. **basin**	base	mason	baking

At Home: Review the Word Study Steps to help the student spell new words.

Name_____

burden	carton	hasten	cable	civil
dwindle	gallon	fumble	normal	novel
basin	whistle	villain	urban	organ
satin	curtain	peril	gravel	dangle

Write the spelling words with each of the spelling patterns below.

-an

1. _____

2. _____

-ain

3. _____

4. _____

-en

5. _____

6. _____

-in

7. _____

8. _____

-on

9. _____

10. _____

-al

11. _____

-el

12. _____

13. _____

-il

14. _____

15. _____

-le

16. _____

17. _____

18. _____

19. _____

20. _____

Name_____

burden	carton	hasten	cable	civil
dwindle	gallon	fumble	normal	novel
basin	whistle	villain	urban	organ
satin	curtain	peril	gravel	dangle

Analogies

Write the spelling word that matches each definition.

1. *16 fluid ounces : one pint* as *128 fluid ounces : one* _____

2. *flower : rose* as *book :* _____

3. *country : rural* as *city :* _____

4. *smooth : rough* as *paved :* _____

5. *police officer : criminal* as *hero :* _____

6. *delay : procrastinate* as *speed :* _____

Sentence Completion

Fill in the blank with the appropriate spelling word.

7. It was a heavy _____ to carry all the luggage at once.

8. When she finished the last of the milk, she threw out the

_____.

9. Now that they have _____ television there are 500 available channels.

10. I must buy a new _____, to block the sun.

11. I think I will buy _____ pajamas because I heard they are very comfortable.

12. The kettle will _____ when the water is boiling.

Spelling

Final *schwa-n*
and *schwa-l*:
Proofreading

Name

Proofreading Activity

There are five spelling mistakes in the paragraph below. Circle the misspelled words. Write the words correctly on the lines below.

Although Earth is mostly water, it contains little that is useable. The amount of water used everyday places a heavy burdin on Earth's natural resources. There are many ways you can reduce the amount of water you waste each day. For example, showering uses less water than filling up the entire bassen for bathing. Placing a milk cartin outside to collect rain water for your indoor plants is another way that you can save water. If we do not make strides toward saving water, we will hassen the destruction of one of our greatest natural resources and the availability of fresh clean useable water may be in perral.

1. _____   3. _____   5. _____

2. _____   4. _____

Writing Activity

There are many things we could do to help save the Earth. Write a short paragraph about a program in your neighborhood that was set up to be environmentally friendly. Use five spelling words.

_____

_____

_____

_____

_____

_____

_____

_____

_____

Name_____

Look at the words in each set below. One word in each set is spelled correctly. Use a pencil to fill in the circle next to the correct word. Before you begin, look at the sample set of words. Sample A has been done for you. Do Sample B by yourself. When you are sure you know what to do, you may go on with the rest of the page.

Sample A:

Ⓐ virtical
Ⓑ vurtical
Ⓒ vertical
Ⓓ vertikal

Sample B:

Ⓔ veterin
Ⓕ veterran
Ⓖ veteran
Ⓗ vertern

1. Ⓐ sivil
   Ⓑ cival
   Ⓒ civil
   Ⓓ civill

2. Ⓔ dwindal
   Ⓕ dwindel
   Ⓖ dwindale
   Ⓗ dwindle

3. Ⓐ novel
   Ⓑ noval
   Ⓒ novell
   Ⓓ novle

4. Ⓔ wistle
   Ⓕ whistel
   Ⓖ whstle
   Ⓗ whistle

5. Ⓐ gravel
   Ⓑ gravil
   Ⓒ gravele
   Ⓓ gravle

6. Ⓔ normal
   Ⓕ normall
   Ⓖ normill
   Ⓗ normil

7. Ⓐ organ
   Ⓑ orgin
   Ⓒ organe
   Ⓓ orgun

8. Ⓔ burrdan
   Ⓕ burdene
   Ⓖ burden
   Ⓗ berden

9. Ⓐ villain
   Ⓑ vilan
   Ⓒ villane
   Ⓓ villin

10. Ⓔ dangull
    Ⓕ dangel
    Ⓖ dangal
    Ⓗ dangle

11. Ⓐ cartin
    Ⓑ carton
    Ⓒ carrton
    Ⓓ cartone

12. Ⓔ erban
    Ⓕ irban
    Ⓖ urrban
    Ⓗ urban

13. Ⓐ peril
    Ⓑ peral
    Ⓒ perill
    Ⓓ perull

14. Ⓔ catin
    Ⓕ satin
    Ⓖ satan
    Ⓗ satun

15. Ⓐ hastin
    Ⓑ hastene
    Ⓒ hasun
    Ⓓ hasten

16. Ⓔ fumbell
    Ⓕ fumbl
    Ⓖ fumbal
    Ⓗ fumble

17. Ⓐ kabel
    Ⓑ kable
    Ⓒ cable
    Ⓓ caball

18. Ⓔ kirtan
    Ⓕ kurtain
    Ⓖ cirtain
    Ⓗ curtain

19. Ⓐ bacin
    Ⓑ basun
    Ⓒ basin
    Ⓓ basen

20. Ⓔ galon
    Ⓕ gallon
    Ⓖ gallun
    Ⓗ gallin

Name _____

Fold back the paper along the dotted line. Write the words in the blanks as they are read aloud. When you finish the test, unfold the paper. Use the list at the right to correct any spelling mistakes.

1. _____
2. _____
3. _____
4. _____
5. _____
6. _____
7. _____
8. _____
9. _____
10. _____
11. _____
12. _____
13. _____
14. _____
15. _____
16. _____
17. _____
18. _____
19. _____
20. _____

Review Words 21. _____
22. _____
23. _____

Challenge Words 24. _____
25. _____

1. unknown
2. incredible
3. superhuman
4. prolong
5. outpost
6. independent
7. incomplete
8. enlist
9. enrich
10. enlarge
11. superstar
12. supermarket
13. outfield
14. outlaw
15. outstanding
16. outcry
17. proclaim
18. uncommon
19. untangle
20. unhook
21. cable
22. gallon
23. curtain
24. indistinct
25. unequal

© Macmillan/McGraw-Hill

At Home: Help the student practice the words he or she missed to prepare for the Posttest.

Name_____

Using the Word Study Steps

1. LOOK at the word.

2. SAY the word aloud.

3. STUDY the letters in the word.

4. WRITE the word.

5. CHECK the word.
   Did you spell the word right?
   If not, go back to step 1.

Alphabetical Order

Write the spelling words in alphabetical order.

1. _____
2. _____
3. _____
4. _____
5. _____
6. _____
7. _____
8. _____
9. _____
10. _____

11. _____
12. _____
13. _____
14. _____
15. _____
16. _____
17. _____
18. _____
19. _____
20. _____

Write the Words

Use the lines below to practice writing the spelling words.

_____ _____ _____

_____ _____ _____

_____ _____ _____

_____ _____ _____

At Home: Review the Word Study Steps to help the student spell new words.

Name_____

unknown	outstanding	incredible	unhook	superhuman
prolong	untangle	outpost	enlist	independent
supermarket	incomplete	enlarge	uncommon	outfield
outcry	enrich	proclaim	outlaw	superstar

Sort the spelling words according to their prefix.

en-

1. _____
2. _____
3. _____

in-

4. _____
5. _____
6. _____

un-

7. _____
8. _____
9. _____
10. _____

super-

11. _____
12. _____
13. _____

pro-

14. _____
15. _____

out-

16. _____
17. _____
18. _____
19. _____
20. _____

Alphabetical Order

Use the lines below to write the spelling words in alphabetical order.

_____ _____ _____ _____

_____ _____ _____ _____

_____ _____ _____ _____

_____ _____ _____ _____

_____ _____ _____ _____

Name_____

unknown	outstanding	incredible	unhook	superhuman
prolong	untangle	outpost	enlist	independent
supermarket	incomplete	enlarge	uncommon	outfield
outcry	enrich	proclaim	outlaw	superstar

Sentence Completion

Fill in the blank with the appropriate spelling word.

1. I need to pick up eggs at the _____.

2. My uncle decided to _____ in the army.

3. The photograph was too small, so I had to _____ it.

4. We watched the baseball game from bleachers in the _____.

5. There was such an _____, that the workers went on strike.

6. The town had to _____ the keeping of wild animals as pets.

Matching Meanings

Write the spelling word that matches each definition.

7. celebrity _____

8. unidentified _____

9. supplement _____

10. self-ruled _____

11. unravel _____

12. lengthen _____

Use the Spelling Words

Write two sentences on the lines below. Use a spelling word in each sentence.

13. _____

14. _____

Name_____

Proofreading Activity

There are five spelling mistakes in the paragraph below. Circle the misspelled words. Write the words correctly on the lines below.

Upon discovery of some unnown artifacts, the town put together a team to uncover the historical significance of their find. Many independant scientists teamed together to untangal the mysteries of the ancient pieces. There was incredable joy when the scientists began to uncover facts about the pieces they discovered. The lead scientist even became a suparstar in the community for his contributions to the project.

1. _____   3. _____   5. _____

2. _____   4. _____

Writing Activity

Write a story about discovering an historical object, perhaps one you found in an attic or basement that revealed something you didn't know about your family. Use five spelling words.

_____

_____

_____

_____

_____

_____

_____

_____

Name_____

Look at the words in each set below. One word in each set is spelled correctly. Use a pencil to fill in the circle next to the correct word. Before you begin, look at the sample set of words. Sample A has been done for you. Do Sample B by yourself. When you are sure you know what to do, you may go on with the rest of the page.

Sample A:

Ⓐ endiscitn
Ⓑ indisstinct
Ⓒ indistinct
Ⓓ indistink

Sample B:

Ⓔ unekaul
Ⓕ unnequal
Ⓖ unequal
Ⓗ unequall

1. Ⓐ unknown
   Ⓑ unnown
   Ⓒ unknon
   Ⓓ unknownn

2. Ⓔ superistar
   Ⓕ supperstar
   Ⓖ superstar
   Ⓗ superstr

3. Ⓐ supirmarkit
   Ⓑ supermarket
   Ⓒ suprmarkit
   Ⓓ supurmarket

4. Ⓔ unkomn
   Ⓕ uncommun
   Ⓖ uncommon
   Ⓗ uncomon

5. Ⓐ outpost
   Ⓑ outposst
   Ⓒ outpst
   Ⓓ outpost

6. Ⓔ outfled
   Ⓕ outfeild
   Ⓖ outfield
   Ⓗ outfild

7. Ⓐ outstandin
   Ⓑ outstanding
   Ⓒ oustanding
   Ⓓ oustanding

8. Ⓔ encredible
   Ⓕ incredable
   Ⓖ incredibel
   Ⓗ incredible

9. Ⓐ independent
   Ⓑ endependent
   Ⓒ inddependent
   Ⓓ independnt

10. Ⓔ untangle
    Ⓕ untangal
    Ⓖ untangel
    Ⓗ untangl

11. Ⓐ outlow
    Ⓑ outlaww
    Ⓒ outlw
    Ⓓ outlaw

12. Ⓔ outkry
    Ⓕ outkri
    Ⓖ outkr
    Ⓗ outcry

13. Ⓐ proclam
    Ⓑ proklain
    Ⓒ proclaim
    Ⓓ proklam

14. Ⓔ inrich
    Ⓕ encirh
    Ⓖ enrich
    Ⓗ enrish

15. Ⓔ enlist
    Ⓕ inlist
    Ⓖ enlisst
    Ⓗ enliss

16. Ⓔ superhuman
    Ⓕ suparhuman
    Ⓖ supperhumn
    Ⓗ seperhewman

17. Ⓐ enlarge
    Ⓑ inlarje
    Ⓒ enlarj
    Ⓓ enlareg

18. Ⓔ prolon
    Ⓕ prolng
    Ⓖ prolawng
    Ⓗ prolong

19. Ⓐ unhuk
    Ⓑ unhook
    Ⓒ unhewk
    Ⓓ unhooc

20. Ⓐ encomplete
    Ⓑ inkomplete
    Ⓒ incomplete
    Ⓓ incomplet

© Macmillan/McGraw-Hill

Name_____

Fold back the paper along the dotted line. Write the words in the blanks as they are read aloud. When you finish the test, unfold the paper. Use the list at the right to correct any spelling mistakes.

1. _____   **1.** inspire
2. _____   **2.** inspiration
3. _____   **3.** consult
4. _____   **4.** consultation
5. _____   **5.** separate
6. _____   **6.** separation
7. _____   **7.** illustrate
8. _____   **8.** illustration
9. _____   **9.** instruct
10. _____   **10.** instruction
11. _____   **11.** observe
12. _____   **12.** observation
13. _____   **13.** react
14. _____   **14.** reaction
15. _____   **15.** connect
16. _____   **16.** connection
17. _____   **17.** hesitate
18. _____   **18.** hesitation
19. _____   **19.** represent
20. _____   **20.** representation

Review Words 21. _____   **21.** incomplete
22. _____   **22.** supermarket
23. _____   **23.** outfield

Challenge Words 24. _____   **24.** evaporate
25. _____   **25.** evaporation

At Home: Help the student practice the words he or she missed to prepare for the Posttest.

The Case of the Phantom Poet
89
Grade 6/Unit 3

Name_____

Using the Word Study Steps

1. LOOK at the word.

2. SAY the word aloud.

3. STUDY the letters in the word.

4. WRITE the word.

5. CHECK the word.
   Did you spell the word right?
   If not, go back to step 1.

Find the Words

Find and circle the spelling words hidden in each set of letters. Then write them on the line provided.

1. r e a c o n n e c t i o b s e r v a   _____

2. t a t i o i n s p i l l u s t r a t e   _____

3. c o n n c o n s u l t a t i n g s a   _____

4. h e s i t a t i o n a t i o n a t s   _____

5. r e p r e a c t i o b s e r v a t i   _____

6. c o u s i n s t r u c t i o n r s a   _____

7. b e s a s e p s e p a r a t i o n   _____

8. r e p r e s e n t a c t i o n e r e   _____

9. n i o t a r o b s e r v a t i o n   _____

10. j u b a n i j i m i n s p i r e   _____

Make a Puzzle

Make up a puzzle of your own using the space on this page. Give it to someone else to solve. Be sure to include at least five spelling words in your puzzle.

At Home: Review the Word Study Steps to help the student spell new words.

Name_____

inspire   inspiration   consult   consultation   separate
separation   illustrate   illustration instruct   instruction
observe   observation   react   reaction   connect
connection   hesitate   hesitation   represent   representation

Sort each spelling word according to how each changes when adding *-ion* or *-ation*. Write the words as follows.

No Suffix

1. _____
2. _____
3. _____
4. _____
5. _____
6. _____
7. _____
8. _____
9. _____
10. _____

Drop final *e* when adding suffix

11. _____
12. _____
13. _____
14. _____
15. _____

Add *-ation*

16. _____
17. _____

Add *-ion*

16. _____
17. _____
18. _____

Write the Words

Use the lines below to practice writing the spelling words.

_____ _____ _____ _____

_____ _____ _____ _____

_____ _____ _____ _____

_____ _____ _____ _____

Name_____

inspire	inspiration	consult	consultation	separate
separation	illustrate	illustration	instruct	instruction
observe	observation	react	reaction	connect
connection	hesitate	hesitation	represent	representation

Sentence Completion

Fill in the blank with the appropriate spelling word.

1. The _____ on the magazine cover was beautiful.

2. I like to _____ the penguins and dolphins at the aquarium.

3. In New Orleans I will _____ to my flight to New York.

4. The doctor offers a free _____ to new patients.

5. Her speech was an _____ to the whole school.

6. If she eats peanuts she will have a strong allergic _____.

7. When my cousins fight, my aunt has to _____ them.

8. During the school fair, I was asked to _____ the art squad.

9. To put the chair together, I had to follow the _____ manual.

10. She did not _____ to ride the scariest rollercoaster.

11. The captain had to _____ his crew on how to set sail.

12. The artist used the computer to _____ the drawings in the book.

13. If you need help with your taxes, you should _____ an accountant.

14. Mr. Rivera made the _____ that the ground was wet.

Name _____

Proofreading Activity

There are five spelling mistakes in the paragraph below. Circle the misspelled words. Write the words correctly on the lines below.

Solving a mystery is often a difficult task. However, with a thorough investigation and careful observattion you may be able to solve the case. First you must seperate fact from fiction, by determining what you know to be true or false. It may be necessary to consult with experts to determine how best to go about solving your mystery. They may be able to offer a conection based on the information you collected, that you may not have noticed at first. Following their instrucsion may make it easier for you to solve your case.

1. _____   3. _____   5. _____

2. _____   4. _____

Writing Activity

Write a set of instruction for a task you know how to do well. Then, trade papers with a partner to check if your instructions are clear to them. Use five spelling words.

_____

_____

_____

_____

_____

_____

_____

_____

Name_____

Look at the words in each set below. One word in each set is spelled correctly. Use a pencil to fill in the circle next to the correct word. Before you begin, look at the sample set of words. Sample A has been done for you. Do Sample B by yourself. When you are sure you know what to do, you may go on with the rest of the page.

Sample A:

- Ⓐ ivaporate
- Ⓑ evaporeight
- Ⓒ evaporate
- Ⓓ evaporite

Sample B:

- Ⓔ ivaporation
- Ⓕ evaporasion
- Ⓖ evaporation
- Ⓗ evaporration

1.
- Ⓐ enstruction
- Ⓑ instruktion
- Ⓒ instrucsion
- Ⓓ instruction

2.
- Ⓔ observation
- Ⓕ obsirvation
- Ⓖ observasion
- Ⓗ observaton

3.
- Ⓐ enspire
- Ⓑ inspre
- Ⓒ inspere
- Ⓓ inspire

4.
- Ⓔ ellustrate
- Ⓕ illustrate
- Ⓖ ilustrate
- Ⓗ illustreight

5.
- Ⓐ hesitasion
- Ⓑ hesitation
- Ⓒ hisitation
- Ⓓ hesatation

6.
- Ⓔ reaktion
- Ⓕ reaction
- Ⓖ reacton
- Ⓗ reacshon

7.
- Ⓐ ensiperation
- Ⓑ inspiration
- Ⓒ insperation
- Ⓓ insparation

8.
- Ⓔ conection
- Ⓕ connection
- Ⓖ konection
- Ⓗ reacshon

9.
- Ⓐ reakt
- Ⓑ recta
- Ⓒ react
- Ⓓ reatc

10.
- Ⓔ reprezent
- Ⓕ reprecent
- Ⓖ represent
- Ⓗ repreesent

11.
- Ⓐ consult
- Ⓑ konsult
- Ⓒ cunsult
- Ⓓ consut

12.
- Ⓔ represintasion
- Ⓕ representation
- Ⓖ representetion
- Ⓗ reprecentation

13.
- Ⓐ consaltation
- Ⓑ consutaion
- Ⓒ consulation
- Ⓓ consultation

14.
- Ⓔ ceparate
- Ⓕ siparate
- Ⓖ separate
- Ⓗ separte

15.
- Ⓐ ceparation
- Ⓑ separition
- Ⓒ separasion
- Ⓓ separation

16.
- Ⓔ abserve
- Ⓕ observ
- Ⓖ observe
- Ⓗ obsirve

17.
- Ⓐ hesatate
- Ⓑ hezitate
- Ⓒ hesetate
- Ⓓ hesitate

18.
- Ⓔ illustration
- Ⓕ elustration
- Ⓖ ilustration
- Ⓗ illustrasion

19.
- Ⓐ connect
- Ⓑ konnect
- Ⓒ conect
- Ⓓ konectt

20.
- Ⓔ renstruct
- Ⓕ enstruckt
- Ⓖ instruckt
- Ⓗ instruct

© Macmillan/McGraw-Hill

Name_____

Read each sentence. If an underlined word is spelled wrong, fill in the circle that goes with that word. If no word is spelled wrong, fill in the circle below NONE. Read Sample A, and do Sample B.

A. When the patron bumped into the <u>wayter</u> the <u>platter</u> he
                                      A   B
carried began to <u>falter</u>.
                  C

NONE
A. Ⓐ Ⓑ Ⓒ Ⓓ

B. The <u>janiter</u> did not <u>hesitate</u> to get to work to <u>install</u> the
       E   F   G
new heating system.

NONE
B. Ⓔ Ⓕ Ⓖ Ⓗ

1. To their <u>dismay</u> the <u>actor</u> was unable to form a
           A   B
<u>connecsion</u> with the audience.
    C

NONE
1. Ⓐ Ⓑ Ⓒ Ⓓ

2. I must stop by the <u>supermarket</u> to pick up <u>vinegar</u> to
                      E   F
<u>flaver</u> the soup.
   G

NONE
2. Ⓔ Ⓕ Ⓖ Ⓗ

3. The quarterback made many <u>incredible</u> plays despite
                             A
one early <u>maneuver</u> that resulted in a <u>fumble</u>.
        B   C

NONE
3. Ⓐ Ⓑ Ⓒ Ⓓ

4. After a <u>consoltation</u> from an interior designer, we
          E
decided to go with a <u>satin</u> <u>curtain</u>.
                 F   G

NONE
4. Ⓔ Ⓕ Ⓖ Ⓗ

5. The <u>welthy</u> man began to <u>prepare</u> for his trip <u>abroad</u>.
      A   B   C

NONE
5. Ⓐ Ⓑ Ⓒ Ⓓ

6. My <u>ancestor</u> wrote a poem on <u>parchment</u> paper that I
     E   F
found to be an <u>inspiration</u>.
           G

NONE
6. Ⓔ Ⓕ Ⓖ Ⓗ

7. The sack of <u>gravel</u> placed a <u>burden</u> on his <u>showlder</u>.
         A   B   C

NONE
7. Ⓐ Ⓑ Ⓒ Ⓓ

Name_____

8. After the <u>orgen</u> transplant he would be quite <u>healthy</u>
          E   F

and not in <u>peril</u>.
            G

8. Ⓔ Ⓕ Ⓖ Ⓗ

9. Henry will <u>react</u> without <u>hesitasion</u> which makes him
              A   B

<u>superhuman</u> in my eyes.
     C

9. Ⓐ Ⓑ Ⓒ Ⓓ

10. <u>Aplaud</u> the <u>outstanding</u> performance of the <u>superstar</u>.
     E   F   G

10. Ⓔ Ⓕ Ⓖ Ⓗ

11. The <u>customer</u> was happy to <u>axept</u> the <u>carton</u> of goods.
         A   B   C

11. Ⓐ Ⓑ Ⓒ Ⓓ

12. The town was <u>repaid</u> for all the money the <u>outlaw</u> was
                  E   F

able to <u>swindle</u>.
         G

12. Ⓔ Ⓕ Ⓖ Ⓗ

13. The <u>traitor</u> could not <u>observe</u> himself in the <u>mirrur</u>.
         A   B   C

13. Ⓐ Ⓑ Ⓒ Ⓓ

14. By learning how to <u>whistle</u>, Danica was able to <u>fulfill</u>
                        E   F

an <u>incomplet</u> dream.
     G

14. Ⓔ Ⓕ Ⓖ Ⓗ

15. City hall could not <u>ignore</u> the <u>civil</u> <u>outcry</u>.
                        A   B   C

15. Ⓐ Ⓑ Ⓒ Ⓓ

16. <u>Untangle</u> the <u>cabal</u> before you <u>connect</u> it.
     E   F   G

16. Ⓔ Ⓕ Ⓖ Ⓗ

17. The <u>observer</u> watched the <u>basin</u> fill with a <u>galun</u>.
         A   B   C

17. Ⓐ Ⓑ Ⓒ Ⓓ

18. The <u>bachelor</u> had a <u>forlorn</u> <u>reaction</u>.
         E   F   G

18. Ⓔ Ⓕ Ⓖ Ⓗ

19. <u>Enlist</u> the best artist to create an <u>illastration</u> for your <u>novel</u>.
     A   B   C

19. Ⓐ Ⓑ Ⓒ Ⓓ

20. <u>Consult</u> a tutor and do not <u>prolong</u> the <u>unnown</u>.
     E   F   G

20. Ⓔ Ⓕ Ⓖ Ⓗ

© Macmillan/McGraw-Hill

Name_____

Fold back the paper along the dotted line. Write the words in the blanks as they are read aloud. When you finish the test, unfold the paper. Use the list at the right to correct any spelling mistakes.

1. _____
2. _____
3. _____
4. _____
5. _____
6. _____
7. _____
8. _____
9. _____
10. _____
11. _____
12. _____
13. _____
14. _____
15. _____
16. _____
17. _____
18. _____
19. _____
20. _____

Review Words 21. _____

22. _____

23. _____

Challenge Words 24. _____

25. _____

1. admit
2. admission
3. permit
4. permission
5. explain
6. explanation
7. exclaim
8. exclamation
9. include
10. inclusion
11. explode
12. explosion
13. divide
14. division
15. decide
16. decision
17. omit
18. omission
19. collide
20. collision
21. separation
22. instruction
23. connection
24. expand
25. expansion

© Macmillan/McGraw-Hill

 At Home: Help the student practice the words he or she missed to prepare for the Posttest.

Name_____

Using the Word Study Steps

1. LOOK at the word.

2. SAY the word aloud.

3. STUDY the letters in the word.

4. WRITE the word.

5. CHECK the word,
   Did you spell the word right?
   If not, go back to step 1.

Missing Letters

Fill in the missing letters to form spelling words.

1. explos _____

2. explan _____

3. _____ laim

4. decis _____

5. exclam _____

6. collis _____

7. _____ cide

8. _____ lode

9. permis _____

10. inclus _____

11. _____ lide

12. admis _____

13. omis _____

14. _____ lude

15. divis _____

At Home: Review the Word Study Steps to help the student
spell new words.

Name_____

admit	admission	permit	permission	explain
explanation	exclaim	exclamation	include	inclusion
explode	explosion	divide	division	decide
decision	omit	omission	collide	collision

Sort by Spelling Changes

t to *ss*-

1. _____ _____

2. _____ _____

3. _____ _____

dropping *i*

4. _____ _____

5. _____ _____

de to *s*

6. _____ _____

7. _____ _____

8. _____ _____

9. _____ _____

10. _____ _____

Write the Words

Use the lines below to practice writing the spelling words.

_____ _____ _____ _____

_____ _____ _____ _____

_____ _____ _____ _____

_____ _____ _____ _____

Name_____

admit	admission	permit	permission	explain
explanation	exclaim	exclamation	include	inclusion
explode	explosion	divide	division	decide
decision	omit	omission	collide	collision

Sentence Completion

Fill in the blank with the appropriate spelling word.

1. With the coupon we were allowed free _____ to the museum.

2. We decided to _____ the profits evenly among the five of us.

3. The car was beyond recognition after the _____.

4. I have to ask my parents for _____ to go to my friend's party.

5. Before the lights went out in the building we heard a loud _____.

6. My grandmother wanted me to _____ to her why I was late for dinner.

7. My little cousin likes it when I _____ her in our basketball games.

8. Pendo and Tiki get upset when their kites _____.

9. Susan needs to obtain a _____ from the park to play tennis.

10. I have to _____ if I want to take swimming or boxing classes.

11. Our teacher decided to _____ our lowest grade on a test.

12. My mom always says it takes a strong person to _____ when they are wrong.

13. You can use an _____ mark to end a sentence that conveys strong emotion.

14. This year in school we will learn long _____.

15. The local theater has to make a _____ on which play they will produce next.

Name_____

Proofreading Activity

There are five spelling mistakes in the paragraph below. Circle the misspelled words. Write the words correctly on the lines below.

After watching a documentary on rock climbers, Raphael made a decition that he would like to try it. He read a book on the subject that gave a clear explanasion of how to train. He asked the coach at his school to inclued him in the school's training team. After several months of training, Raphael felt confident enough to ask his coach for permision to tryout for the rock climbing team at the local gym. His coach agreed and Raphael was so happy after the tryouts to learn that the gym would addmit him to the rock climbing competition. For Raphael, his dedication to making the competition was more impressive and rewarding than whether or not he won.

1. _____   2. _____   3. _____

4. _____   5. _____

Writing Activity

Have you ever worked really hard to try to achieve a specific goal? Write a short paragraph about a goal that required determination to achieve. Use five spelling words.

_____

_____

_____

_____

_____

_____

_____

Look at the words in each set below. One word in each set is spelled correctly. Use a pencil to fill in the circle next to the correct word. Before you begin, look at the sample set of words. Sample A has been done for you. Do Sample B by yourself. When you are sure you know what to do, you may go on with the rest of the page.

Sample A:

- Ⓐ xpand
- Ⓑ expan
- Ⓒ expand
- Ⓓ expadn

Sample B:

- Ⓔ expansion
- Ⓕ xpantion
- Ⓖ expantion
- Ⓗ expannsion

1. Ⓐ addmit
   Ⓑ admitt
   Ⓒ admit
   Ⓓ admt

2. Ⓔ pirmission
   Ⓕ permision
   Ⓖ permission
   Ⓗ pirmission

3. Ⓐ exclaimation
   Ⓑ axclamation
   Ⓒ exclamasion
   Ⓓ exclamation

4. Ⓔ ixplain
   Ⓕ explan
   Ⓖ explian
   Ⓗ explain

5. Ⓐ explode
   Ⓑ ixplode
   Ⓒ explood
   Ⓓ exploed

6. Ⓔ inclusion
   Ⓕ enklusion
   Ⓖ enclusion
   Ⓗ inklusion

7. Ⓐ devide
   Ⓑ divide
   Ⓒ davide
   Ⓓ divied

8. Ⓔ kolide
   Ⓕ collide
   Ⓖ kollide
   Ⓗ colide

9. Ⓐ omission
   Ⓑ amision
   Ⓒ omistion
   Ⓓ omissiun

10. Ⓔ amit
    Ⓕ omitt
    Ⓖ omiet
    Ⓗ omit

11. Ⓐ desicion
    Ⓑ dacision
    Ⓒ decisun
    Ⓓ decision

12. Ⓔ collision
    Ⓕ kollision
    Ⓖ colision
    Ⓗ collition

13. Ⓐ addmtion
    Ⓑ addmission
    Ⓒ admission
    Ⓓ admession

14. Ⓔ devision
    Ⓕ divition
    Ⓖ division
    Ⓗ devision

15. Ⓐ pirmit
    Ⓑ permit
    Ⓒ permitt
    Ⓓ permt

16. Ⓔ explanation
    Ⓕ explaination
    Ⓖ explanasion
    Ⓗ explunation

17. Ⓐ enclude
    Ⓑ inclewd
    Ⓒ include
    Ⓓ inclded

18. Ⓔ xplosion
    Ⓕ explosion
    Ⓖ explotion
    Ⓗ exploshun

19. Ⓐ decide
    Ⓑ dacide
    Ⓒ deside
    Ⓓ decied

20. Ⓔ exklaim
    Ⓕ exclaim
    Ⓖ excliam
    Ⓗ exclaime

© Macmillan/McGraw-Hill

Name_____

Fold back the paper along the dotted line. Write the words in the blanks as they are read aloud. When you finish the test, unfold the paper. Use the list at the right to correct any spelling mistakes.

1. _____
2. _____
3. _____
4. _____
5. _____
6. _____
7. _____
8. _____
9. _____
10. _____
11. _____
12. _____
13. _____
14. _____
15. _____
16. _____
17. _____
18. _____
19. _____
20. _____

Review Words 21. _____
22. _____
23. _____

Challenge Words 24. _____
25. _____

1. vocalize
2. explosive
3. recognize
4. passage
5. storage
6. modernize
7. positive
8. negative
9. criticize
10. organize
11. creative
12. realize
13. advantage
14. attractive
15. percentage
16. emphasize
17. wreckage
18. specialize
19. sympathize
20. secretive
21. permission
22. explanation
23. decision
24. progressive
25. scrutinize

© Macmillan/McGraw-Hill

At Home: Help the student practice the words he or she missed to prepare for the Posttest.

Name_____

Using the Word Study Steps

1. LOOK at the word.

2. SAY the word aloud.

3. STUDY the letters in the word.

4. WRITE the word.

5. CHECK the word. Did you spell the word right? If not, go back to step 1.

Crossword Puzzle

Use the clues to complete the puzzle.

ACROSS

1. My grandfather likes to _____ ideas he finds important.

6. We put the extra furniture into _____.

8. The flowers and the art work helped to make the room more _____.

9. Min was upset about the _____ feedback on her art project.

DOWN

1. Fireworks are highly _____.

2. The explorers were looking for a new _____ to Asia.

3. Preparing for the exam proved to be a huge _____.

4. I joined the art club to explore my _____ talents.

5. The class was very _____ when planning the surprise party.

7. On my last visit to the planetarium, I began to _____ how fascinating the solar system is

At Home: Review the Word Study Steps to help the student spell new words.

Name_____

vocalize	explosive	recognize	passage	storage
modernize	positive	negative	criticize	organize
creative	realize	advantage	attractive	percentage
emphasize	wreckage	specialize	sympathize	secretive

Write the spelling words by word ending.

-age

1. _____
2. _____
3. _____
4. _____
5. _____

-ive

6. _____
7. _____
8. _____
9. _____
10. _____
11. _____

-ize

12. _____
13. _____
14. _____
15. _____
16. _____
17. _____
18. _____
19. _____
20. _____

Alphabetical Order

Use the lines below to write the spelling words in alphabetical order.

_____   _____   _____   _____

_____   _____   _____   _____

_____   _____   _____   _____

_____   _____   _____   _____

_____   _____   _____   _____

Name_____

vocalize	explosive	recognize	passage	storage
modernize	positive	negative	criticize	organize
creative	realize	advantage	attractive	percentage
emphasize	wreckage	specialize	sympathize	secretive

Synonyms

Write the spelling word that matches each synonym.

1. optimistic _____

2. pathway _____

3. harmful _____

4. recite _____

5. focus _____

6. volatile _____

7. fraction _____

8. commiserate _____

9. mysterious _____

10. systematize _____

11. benefit _____

12. condemn _____

13. imaginative _____

14. update _____

15. appealing _____

Name _____

Proofreading Activity

There are five spelling mistakes in the paragraph below. Circle the misspelled words. Write the words correctly on the lines below.

Carmen found that the interests she had as a child were instrumental in choosing a career as an adult. The ocean and beach by her home allowed her the advantige to explore her interest's in marine life. She soon began to reelize that one day she hoped to pursue a career in which she could study these animals. She learned a lot through books and could reconize all the animal life she saw at the beach near her home. She continued to study and eventually became a biologist. She went on to spesalize in marine biology. Carmen found that growing up near the ocean was a very positiv experience for her chosen career.

1. _____   2. _____   3. _____

4. _____   5. _____

Writing Activity

What do you like to do more than anything? Write a story about how you might take this passion and turn it into a career. Use five spelling words.

_____

_____

_____

_____

_____

_____

_____

Name_____

Look at the words in each set below. One word in each set is spelled correctly. Use a pencil to fill in the circle next to the correct word. Before you begin, look at the sample set of words. Sample A has been done for you. Do Sample B by yourself. When you are sure you know what to do, you may go on with the rest of the page.

Sample A:
- Ⓐ progresuve
- Ⓑ progresive
- Ⓒ progressive
- Ⓓ prograssive

Sample B:
- Ⓔ skrutinize
- Ⓕ screwtanize
- Ⓖ scrutinize
- Ⓗ scrutanize

1. Ⓐ voculize
   Ⓑ vocilize
   Ⓒ vocalize
   Ⓓ vocalise

2. Ⓔ rekognize
   Ⓕ rekognise
   Ⓖ recognize
   Ⓗ recognise

3. Ⓐ creative
   Ⓑ kreative
   Ⓒ cretive
   Ⓓ creativv

4. Ⓔ storige
   Ⓕ storaje
   Ⓖ storage
   Ⓗ storuge

5. Ⓐ uttractive
   Ⓑ attractive
   Ⓒ attraktive
   Ⓓ atractive

6. Ⓔ wreckage
   Ⓕ reckage
   Ⓖ wrecage
   Ⓗ wrecaje

7. Ⓐ sympathize
   Ⓑ sympathise
   Ⓒ simpathize
   Ⓓ cympathize

8. Ⓔ pasage
   Ⓕ passage
   Ⓖ pasaje
   Ⓗ passuge

9. Ⓐ realize
   Ⓑ realise
   Ⓒ eelise
   Ⓓ reelize

10. Ⓔ positive
    Ⓕ pozitive
    Ⓖ posutive
    Ⓗ posetive

11. Ⓐ kriticize
    Ⓑ critisize
    Ⓒ criticize
    Ⓓ critacize

12. Ⓔ orrganize
    Ⓕ organize
    Ⓖ organise
    Ⓗ orgunize

13. Ⓐ cecretive
    Ⓑ cekretive
    Ⓒ sekretive
    Ⓓ secretive

14. Ⓔ advantaje
    Ⓕ advantige
    Ⓖ advantaeg
    Ⓗ advantage

15. Ⓐ imphasise
    Ⓑ emphasize
    Ⓒ emphasise
    Ⓓ emphasiez

16. Ⓔ ixplocine
    Ⓕ explocine
    Ⓖ xplosive
    Ⓗ explosive

17. Ⓐ spesialise
    Ⓑ specialise
    Ⓒ spechilize
    Ⓓ specialize

18. Ⓔ modernize
    Ⓕ modurnize
    Ⓖ moderrnize
    Ⓗ moredenize

19. Ⓐ negative
    Ⓑ negitive
    Ⓒ negutive
    Ⓓ negetive

20. Ⓔ pirsentage
    Ⓕ persentige
    Ⓖ percentage
    Ⓗ pircentage

© Macmillan/McGraw-Hill

Name _____

Fold back the paper along the dotted line. Write the words in the blanks as they are read aloud. When you finish the test, unfold the paper. Use the list at the right to correct any spelling mistakes.

1. _____
2. _____
3. _____
4. _____
5. _____
6. _____
7. _____
8. _____
9. _____
10. _____
11. _____
12. _____
13. _____
14. _____
15. _____
16. _____
17. _____
18. _____
19. _____
20. _____

Review Words 21. _____
22. _____
23. _____

Challenge Words 24. _____
25. _____

1. unfairness
2. disgraceful
3. unsuccessful
4. outlandish
5. outsider
6. discouragement
7. incorrectly
8. enforcement
9. reminder
10. enclosure
11. unselfish
12. delightful
13. unevenly
14. disapproval
15. disappointment
16. repayment
17. designer
18. departure
19. unhappiness
20. enjoyment
21. passage
22. positive
23. realize
24. displeasure
25. informal

At Home: Help the student practice the words he or she missed to prepare for the Posttest.

© Macmillan/McGraw-Hill

Name_____

Using the Word Study Steps

1. LOOK at the word.

2. SAY the word aloud.

3. STUDY the letters in the word.

4. WRITE the word.

5. CHECK the word.
Did you spell the word right?
If not, go back to step 1.

Alphabetical Order

Write the spelling words in alphabetical order.

1. _____
2. _____
3. _____
4. _____
5. _____
6. _____
7. _____
8. _____
9. _____
10. _____

11. _____
12. _____
13. _____
14. _____
15. _____
16. _____
17. _____
18. _____
19. _____
20. _____

Write the Words

Use the lines below to practice writing the spelling words.

_____ _____ _____ _____

_____ _____ _____ _____

_____ _____ _____ _____

_____ _____ _____ _____

_____ _____ _____ _____

© Macmillan/McGraw-Hill

At Home: Review the Word Study Steps to help the student spell new words.

Name_____

unfairness	disgraceful	unsuccessful	outlandish	outsider
discouragement	incorrectly	enforcement	reminder	enclosure
unselfish	delightful	unevenly	disapproval	repayment
disappointment	designer	departure	unhappiness	enjoyment

Sort the spelling words according to their prefix and suffix.

de-
1. _____
2. _____
3. _____

dis-
4. _____
5. _____
6. _____
7. _____

en-
8. _____
9. _____
10. _____

in-
11. _____

out-
12. _____
13. _____

re-
14. _____
15. _____

un-
16. _____
17. _____
18. _____
19. _____
20. _____

-al
21. _____

-er
22. _____
23. _____
24. _____

-ful
25. _____
26. _____
27. _____

-ish
28. _____
29. _____

-ly
30. _____
31. _____

-ment
32. _____
33. _____
34. _____
35. _____
36. _____

-ness
37. _____
38. _____

-ure
39. _____
40. _____

© Macmillan/McGraw-Hill

Name_____

unfairness	disgraceful	unsuccessful	outlandish	outsider
discouragement	incorrectly	enforcement	reminder	enclosure
unselfish	delightful	unevenly	disapproval	repayment
disappointment	designer	departure	unhappiness	enjoyment

Matching Meanings

Write the spelling word that matches each definition.

1. wrong, false or inaccurate _____

2. dislike somebody or something _____

3. a boundary surrounding something _____

4. not resulting in a favorable outcome _____

5. setting off on an expedition _____

6. not equal or just _____

7. a sum of money paid back to a lender _____

8. to compel obedience of the law _____

9. a feeling of sadness or irritation _____

10. somebody who is not part of the group _____

11. something that you are ashamed of _____

12. pleasure derived from an experience _____

13. something that is used so as not to forget _____

14. bizarre or extremely unusual _____

15. somebody who makes or uses design _____

Name_____

Proofreading Activity

There are five spelling mistakes in the paragraph below. Circle the misspelled words. Write the words correctly on the lines below.

Jude experienced great unhappyness when he failed his science exam. He failed because he answered most of the questions incorrectley. When his friends were discussing how well they had done on the exam, Jude felt like an outsidr. His teacher told him that he should not feel discoragment toward the class. His teacher felt that if Jude studied extra hard for the next exam he would be able to experience the injoyment of doing well in the class. Jude's teacher turned out to be correct. Jude studied hard and asked for extra help for the next exam and did very well.

1. _____   2. _____   3. _____

4. _____   5. _____

Writing Activity

Did you ever feel like you had to work twice as hard for something that came more easily to a friend? Write a story about the experience and what you learned from it. Use five spelling words.

_____

_____

_____

_____

_____

_____

_____

_____

_____

Look at the words in each set below. One word in each set is spelled correctly. Use a pencil to fill in the circle next to the correct word. Before you begin, look at the sample set of words. Sample A has been done for you. Do Sample B by yourself. When you are sure you know what to do, you may go on with the rest of the page.

Sample A:

Ⓐ dizpleasure
Ⓑ disspleasure
Ⓒ displeasure
Ⓓ displesure

Sample B:

Ⓔ informall
Ⓕ enformal
Ⓖ informal
Ⓗ innformal

1. Ⓐ unfareness
Ⓑ unfarness
Ⓒ unfairnez
Ⓓ unfairness

2. Ⓔ encorrectly
Ⓕ incorrectly
Ⓖ enkorectly
Ⓗ encorectly

3. Ⓐ unsuccessful
Ⓑ unnsucessfull
Ⓒ unsucesfull
Ⓓ unsuccessfull

4. Ⓔ unselfish
Ⓕ unsellfish
Ⓖ unselfsh
Ⓗ uncellfish

5. Ⓐ delitful
Ⓑ delightfull
Ⓒ delightful
Ⓓ deliteful

6. Ⓔ outsider
Ⓕ outsidir
Ⓖ outsidr
Ⓗ outsidder

7. Ⓐ inforsement
Ⓑ enforsement
Ⓒ enforcement
Ⓓ enforcment

8. Ⓔ owtlandish
Ⓕ outlandesh
Ⓖ outlandush
Ⓗ outlandish

9. Ⓐ repament
Ⓑ repaymint
Ⓒ repayment
Ⓓ repaymnt

10. Ⓔ designer
Ⓕ deziner
Ⓖ designir
Ⓗ designa

11. Ⓐ diskouragement
Ⓑ discorogemnt
Ⓒ discouragement
Ⓓ discuragment

12. Ⓔ disappoint
Ⓕ desappoint
Ⓖ disapointmint
Ⓗ disappointment

13. Ⓐ injoymint
Ⓑ enjoyment
Ⓒ enjoymint
Ⓓ enjayment

14. Ⓔ unevanly
Ⓕ unevenly
Ⓖ unevenlee
Ⓗ unevunly

15. Ⓐ deepartur
Ⓑ departure
Ⓒ depature
Ⓓ depparture

16. Ⓔ dizgracful
Ⓕ disgraceful
Ⓖ disgracefull
Ⓗ dissgracefull

17. Ⓐ reminder
Ⓑ remindr
Ⓒ remindir
Ⓓ remindur

18. Ⓔ inclosure
Ⓕ enclosure
Ⓖ enclosire
Ⓗ enklosure

19. Ⓐ dissaproval
Ⓑ disaproval
Ⓒ disapprovil
Ⓓ disapproval

20. Ⓔ unhappiness
Ⓕ unhappeness
Ⓖ unhappyness
Ⓗ unhappyniss

Name_____

Fold back the paper along the dotted line. Write the words in the blanks as they are read aloud. When you finish the test, unfold the paper. Use the list at the right to correct any spelling mistakes.

1. _____
2. _____
3. _____
4. _____
5. _____
6. _____
7. _____
8. _____
9. _____
10. _____
11. _____
12. _____
13. _____
14. _____
15. _____
16. _____
17. _____
18. _____
19. _____
20. _____

Review Words 21. _____
22. _____
23. _____

Challenge Words 24. _____
25. _____

1. compete
2. competition
3. metal
4. metallic
5. final
6. finally
7. nation
8. national
9. moment
10. momentous
11. crime
12. criminal
13. reside
14. resident
15. origin
16. original
17. ignite
18. ingition
19. refer
20. reference
21. incorrectly
22. departure
23. unhappiness
24. acquire
25. acquisition

At Home: Help the student practice the words he or she missed to prepare for the Posttest.

Name_____

Using the Word Study Steps

1. LOOK at the word.

2. SAY the word aloud.

3. STUDY the letters in the word.

4. WRITE the word.

5. CHECK the word.
   Did you spell the word right?
   If not, go back to step 1.

Find Rhyming Words

Circle the word in each row that rhymes with the spelling word on the left.

1. **metal**	settle	retail	hospital
2. **refer**	suffer	occur	after
3. **reside**	cupid	rustle	divide
4. **competition**	completion	position	missile
5. **national**	notional	emotional	rational
6. **momentous**	momentum	delicious	apprentice
7. **ignition**	function	caution	musician
8. **compete**	discrete	abrupt	create
9. **crime**	team	rhyme	lemon
10. **reference**	deference	prance	clearance
11. **finality**	jollity	morality	frailty
12. **nation**	station	mission	suction
13. **ignite**	delight	crate	align
14. **final**	regal	little	vinyl
15. **original**	petal	cable	aboriginal

© Macmillan/McGraw-Hill

At Home: Review the Word Study Steps to help the student spell new words.

Name

compete	competition	metal	metallic	final
finality	nation	national	moment	momentous
crime	criminal	reside	resident	origin
original	ignite	ignition	refer	reference

Alphabetical Order

Write the spelling words in alphabetical order.

1. _____   11. _____

2. _____   12. _____

3. _____   13. _____

4. _____   14. _____

5. _____   15. _____

6. _____   16. _____

7. _____   17. _____

8. _____   18. _____

9. _____   19. _____

10. _____   20. _____

Make a Puzzle

Make up a puzzle of your own using the space on this page. Give it to someone else to solve. Be sure to include at least five spelling words in your puzzle.

Name_____

compete	competition	metal	metallic	final
finality	nation	national	moment	momentous
crime	criminal	reside	resident	origin
original	ignite	ignition	refer	reference

Sentence Completion

Fill in the blank with the appropriate spelling word.

1. The bald eagle is our _____ bird.

2. There were seven _____ members in the jazz band.

3. The police officer worked very hard to try to capture the _____.

4. Mo's birthday was a _____ occasion.

5. You have to put the key in the _____ to start the car.

6. The coach asked me to _____ in the state track races.

7. The _____ ring was more expensive than the plastic one.

8. I used a match to _____ the wood for the bonfire.

9. Winning the spelling bee was a great _____ in my life.

10. I _____ in a four story brick building.

11. Dylan needed to list a personal _____ on his job application.

12. Sunset red was the _____ color I picked to paint my room.

13. The Safety Force is a group of superheroes that fight _____.

14. I practiced for several weeks to prepare for the gymnastic

   _____.

15. A local _____ was given an award for her contributions to the town.

Name_____

Proofreading Activity

There are five spelling mistakes in the paragraph below. Circle the misspelled words. Write the words correctly on the lines below.

Today was a truly momentis occasion in my life. I was so happy because I won a qualifying race of the nasional bike tournament for children. The compitition was eight miles long. We raced through the streets of the neighborhood in which I rezide. During the finle mile I knew I was winning because there was nobody racing near me. I was so proud when I won.

1. _____   2. _____   3. _____

4. _____   5. _____

Writing Activity

What's one accomplishment that you are very proud of? Write a diary entry about your accomplishment and what made it special. Use five spelling words.

_____

_____

_____

_____

_____

_____

_____

_____

_____

Name_____

Look at the words in each set below. One word in each set is spelled correctly. Use a pencil to fill in the circle next to the correct word. Before you begin, look at the sample set of words. Sample A has been done for you. Do Sample B by yourself. When you are sure you know what to do, you may go on with the rest of the page.

Sample A:

- Ⓐ acquire
- Ⓑ akuire
- Ⓒ uckuire
- Ⓓ ackuire

Sample B:

- Ⓔ akuisition
- Ⓕ acquisition
- Ⓖ accweesition
- Ⓗ acquizishon

1.
- Ⓐ compeet
- Ⓑ compet
- Ⓒ compete
- Ⓓ kompete

2.
- Ⓔ momentus
- Ⓕ momentous
- Ⓖ momintous
- Ⓗ momentaus

3.
- Ⓐ finaly
- Ⓑ finalle
- Ⓒ finale
- Ⓓ finally

4.
- Ⓔ nasional
- Ⓕ nationull
- Ⓖ national
- Ⓗ nationul

5.
- Ⓐ metalic
- Ⓑ metallik
- Ⓒ matallic
- Ⓓ metallic

6.
- Ⓔ ignision
- Ⓕ ignetion
- Ⓖ igniton
- Ⓗ ignition

7.
- Ⓐ fynil
- Ⓑ finil
- Ⓒ final
- Ⓓ finull

8.
- Ⓔ orijinull
- Ⓕ original
- Ⓖ originale
- Ⓗ originull

9.
- Ⓐ refer
- Ⓑ rafer
- Ⓒ reffer
- Ⓓ referr

10.
- Ⓔ rezident
- Ⓕ resident
- Ⓖ resudent
- Ⓗ residunt

11.
- Ⓐ momentt
- Ⓑ moment
- Ⓒ momunt
- Ⓓ momment

12.
- Ⓔ awrigin
- Ⓕ orijin
- Ⓖ origine
- Ⓗ origin

13.
- Ⓐ egnite
- Ⓑ ignight
- Ⓒ ignitt
- Ⓓ ignite

14.
- Ⓔ krime
- Ⓕ crimm
- Ⓖ criem
- Ⓗ crime

15.
- Ⓐ refference
- Ⓑ referunce
- Ⓒ referance
- Ⓓ reference

16.
- Ⓔ metil
- Ⓕ metal
- Ⓖ metull
- Ⓗ metale

17.
- Ⓐ nasion
- Ⓑ nation
- Ⓒ nattion
- Ⓓ natoin

18.
- Ⓔ kompatition
- Ⓕ compatition
- Ⓖ competition
- Ⓗ competision

19.
- Ⓐ criminull
- Ⓑ criminal
- Ⓒ crimenal
- Ⓓ kriminal

20.
- Ⓔ rezide
- Ⓕ residde
- Ⓖ reside
- Ⓗ resied

© Macmillan/McGraw-Hill

Name_____

Fold back the paper along the dotted line. Write the words in the blanks as they are read aloud. When you finish the test, unfold the paper. Use the list at the right to correct any spelling mistakes.

1. _____
2. _____
3. _____
4. _____
5. _____
6. _____
7. _____
8. _____
9. _____
10. _____
11. _____
12. _____
13. _____
14. _____
15. _____
16. _____
17. _____
18. _____
19. _____
20. _____

Review Words 21. _____
22. _____
23. _____

Challenge Words 24. _____
25. _____

1. crumb
2. crumble
3. design
4. designate
5. solemn
6. solemnity
7. muscle
8. muscular
9. reject
10. rejection
11. create
12. creation
13. public
14. publicity
15. prejudice
16. prejudicial
17. magic
18. magician
19. office
20. official
21. competition
22. criminal
23. resident
24. complicate
25. complication

At Home: Help the student practice the words he or she missed to prepare for the Posttest.

A Single Shard • Grade 6/Unit 4   121

Name_____

Using the Word Study Steps

1. LOOK at the word.

2. SAY the word aloud.

3. STUDY the letters in the word.

4. WRITE the word.

5. CHECK the word.
   Did you spell the word right?
   If not, go back to step 1.

Find the Words

Find and circle the spelling words hidden in each set of letters.

1. m a g i c r e a t e n a t e l y   _____

2. p u b l i c i t r e j e c i a l   _____

3. p u b p r e j u d i c i a l e t e   _____

4. m u s c u l s o l e m n a t e   _____

5. p r e j u d i c e a t i o n   _____

6. c r e a t c r u m b i l i o n   _____

7. d e s i n g i n g o f f i c i a l   _____

8. m u s c u l a r e a l i t r a t e   _____

9. p r e d e s i g n a t i l i t y   _____

10. o f f i c e a l a r p u b i a t e   _____

11. s o l e m m u s c l e a t l y   _____

12. r e j e c r e j e c t i n a l i c e   _____

13. c r u m a g i c a b l e u l a r   _____

14. c r e a t i o n o f f i c u l a t e   _____

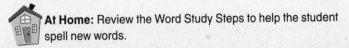

At Home: Review the Word Study Steps to help the student spell new words.

© Macmillan/McGraw-Hill

Name _____

crumb	crumble	design	designate	solemn
solemnity	muscle	muscular	reject	rejection
create	creation	public	publicity	prejudice
prejudicial	magic	magician	office	official

Sort the spelling words by consonant sound changes.

silent/sounded

1. _____ _____
2. _____ _____
3. _____ _____
4. _____ _____

/t/ to /sh/

5. _____ _____
6. _____ _____

/k/ to /sh/

7. _____ _____

/k/ to /s/

8. _____ _____

/s/ to /sh/

9. _____ _____
10. _____ _____

Name_____

crumb	crumble	design	designate	solemn
solemnity	muscle	muscular	reject	rejection
create	creation	public	publicity	prejudice
prejudicial	magic	magician	office	official

Word Meanings

Write the spelling word that matches each definition.

1. to give something a name   _____

2. physically strong   _____

3. to break up into small bits   _____

4. a place where work is conducted   _____

5. advertising used to create interest   _____

6. making something exist   _____

7. tricks and illusions   _____

8. a very small piece of bread   _____

9. to do with people or the community   _____

10. a plan used in the creation of something   _____

11. a person in an authoritative position   _____

12. a person who does tricks or illusions   _____

13. conducting oneself as serious or sincere   _____

14. preconceived ideas about a person   _____

15. to refuse to accept something   _____

Name_____

Proofreading Activity

There are five spelling mistakes in the paragraph below. Circle the misspelled words. Write the words correctly on the lines below.

One day during the summer Maxwell sat in the park with a group of friends and showed them the new magick tricks he had learned. His friends were impressed with his new skills and soon a crowd of people had formed to watch Maxwell perform. Maxwell decided that this would be a good way to spend his summer. He decided to dezignate a specific place and time each day when he would perform his show. To make it oficial he asked his sister to help him dezine a poster. The poster said "Every day at 4:00 on the Great Lawn in Panorama Park come witness the amazing talents of Maxwell the Master Magition."

1. _____   2. _____   3. _____
4. _____   5. _____

Writing Activity

Have you ever turned your talents into a rewarding job? Write a story about a talent that you would like to use in your career. Use at least five spelling words.

_____
_____
_____
_____
_____
_____
_____
_____

Name_____

Look at the words in each set below. One word in each set is spelled correctly. Use a pencil to fill in the circle next to the correct word. Before you begin, look at the sample set of words. Sample A has been done for you. Do Sample B by yourself. When you are sure you know what to do, you may go on with the rest of the page.

Sample A:

Ⓐ komplicate
Ⓑ compliceight
Ⓒ complicate
Ⓓ cawmplicate

Sample B:

Ⓔ komplicasion
Ⓕ complcation
Ⓖ cawmplication
Ⓗ complication

1. Ⓐ krumb
   Ⓑ crumb
   Ⓒ krum
   Ⓓ crammb

2. Ⓔ krumble
   Ⓕ crumbel
   Ⓖ krumbel
   Ⓗ crumble

3. Ⓐ publicity
   Ⓑ publisity
   Ⓒ publicitee
   Ⓓ publicuty

4. Ⓔ solumnity
   Ⓕ solenity
   Ⓖ solemnaty
   Ⓗ solemnity

5. Ⓐ muskulir
   Ⓑ muskular
   Ⓒ musculir
   Ⓓ muscular

6. Ⓔ rejektion
   Ⓕ rejecsion
   Ⓖ rejectun
   Ⓗ rejection

7. Ⓐ creasion
   Ⓑ kreation
   Ⓒ creation
   Ⓓ kreasion

8. Ⓔ dezignate
   Ⓕ decignate
   Ⓖ desugnate
   Ⓗ designate

9. Ⓐ oficial
   Ⓑ offishall
   Ⓒ official
   Ⓓ oficiale

10. Ⓔ prejudisial
    Ⓕ pregudicial
    Ⓖ prejudicial
    Ⓗ prejudishall

11. Ⓐ majcian
    Ⓑ majician
    Ⓒ magician
    Ⓓ magision

12. Ⓔ publik
    Ⓕ pablic
    Ⓖ public
    Ⓗ publuc

13. Ⓐ offise
    Ⓑ office
    Ⓒ ofice
    Ⓓ offuse

14. Ⓔ muscle
    Ⓕ musle
    Ⓖ mussl
    Ⓗ muscell

15. Ⓐ majic
    Ⓑ magic
    Ⓒ magik
    Ⓓ magick

16. Ⓔ create
    Ⓕ kreate
    Ⓖ creight
    Ⓗ creete

17. Ⓐ design
    Ⓑ dezign
    Ⓒ desen
    Ⓓ desine

18. Ⓔ solemn
    Ⓕ solem
    Ⓖ solum
    Ⓗ solenm

19. Ⓐ pregudise
    Ⓑ prejudice
    Ⓒ prejudize
    Ⓓ prejadice

20. Ⓔ reject
    Ⓕ rejeckt
    Ⓖ rrejekt
    Ⓗ regect

Read each sentence. If an underlined word is spelled wrong, fill in the circle that goes with that word. If no word is spelled wrong, fill in the circle below NONE. Read Sample A and do Sample B.

NONE

A. Julian felt <u>disappointment</u> and <u>unhappyness</u> when he   **A.** Ⓐ ⬤ Ⓒ Ⓓ
                              A   B

lost the <u>competition</u>.
                    C

NONE

B. The <u>designer</u> was delighted to <u>realize</u> his <u>creativ</u> talents. **B.** Ⓔ Ⓕ Ⓖ Ⓗ
                E   F   G

NONE

1. After the <u>collision</u> there was an <u>explosion</u> in the <u>reckage</u>. **1.** Ⓐ Ⓑ Ⓒ Ⓓ
                         A   B   C

NONE

2. They decided to <u>modernize</u> the room with a <u>metallic</u> <u>dezign</u>. **2.** Ⓔ Ⓕ Ⓖ Ⓗ
                              E   F   G

NONE

3. I felt <u>discouragment</u> from the <u>negative</u> feedback and **3.** Ⓐ Ⓑ Ⓒ Ⓓ
                   A   B

<u>disapproval</u>.
       C

NONE

4. Dayshawn <u>incorectly</u> answered four questions on his **4.** Ⓔ Ⓕ Ⓖ Ⓗ
                      E

math <u>final</u> on long <u>division</u>.
          F   G

NONE

5. The <u>criminel</u> committed a <u>disgraceful</u> <u>crime</u>. **5.** Ⓐ Ⓑ Ⓒ Ⓓ
               A   B   C

NONE

6. The <u>enclosure</u> was set up for the <u>national</u> <u>office</u>. **6.** Ⓔ Ⓕ Ⓖ Ⓗ
               E   F   G

NONE

7. The <u>outsider</u> was questioned about his <u>nation</u> of <u>origen</u>. **7.** Ⓐ Ⓑ Ⓒ Ⓓ
               A   B   C

NONE

8. Please <u>vocalize</u> an <u>explaination</u> concerning your <u>decision</u> **8.** Ⓔ Ⓕ Ⓖ Ⓗ
                  E   F   G

NONE

9. Kelly felt the <u>rejection</u> of his application for <u>admition</u> was **9.** Ⓐ Ⓑ Ⓒ Ⓓ
                         A   B

based on <u>prejudice</u>.
                 C

Name_____

10. When the <u>magician</u> decided to <u>ignight</u> the prop, the
             E   F

crowd feared it would <u>explode</u>.
                 G

NONE
10. Ⓔ Ⓕ Ⓖ Ⓗ

11. The <u>original</u> façade at the place where I <u>reside</u> is
           A   B

beginning to <u>crumble</u>.
         C

NONE
11. Ⓐ Ⓑ Ⓒ Ⓓ

12. It was a <u>deliteful</u> <u>moment</u> when the bird ate the <u>crumb</u>.
              E   F   G

NONE
12. Ⓔ Ⓕ Ⓖ Ⓗ

13. A <u>resident</u> in my building has an <u>attractive</u> <u>muscular</u>
          A   B   C

physique.

NONE
13. Ⓐ Ⓑ Ⓒ Ⓓ

14. Do not <u>permit</u> those with an unfair <u>advantage</u> to <u>compeet</u>.
             E   F   G

NONE
14. Ⓔ Ⓕ Ⓖ Ⓗ

15. I had to <u>organise</u> the furniture in order to <u>designate</u>
              A   B

what should be placed in <u>storage</u>.
                    C

NONE
15. Ⓐ Ⓑ Ⓒ Ⓓ

16. A large <u>percentage</u> of the <u>public</u> rejected the plans to
              E   F

<u>kreate</u> a new town hall.
 G

NONE
16. Ⓔ Ⓕ Ⓖ Ⓗ

17. Alma had an <u>exclamasion</u> of <u>enjoyment</u> when she could <u>divide</u>.
                A   B   C

NONE
17. Ⓐ Ⓑ Ⓒ Ⓓ

18. He had to consult the <u>refereance</u> to <u>explain</u> the <u>muscle</u> purpose.
                  E   F   G

NONE
18. Ⓔ Ⓕ Ⓖ Ⓗ

19. I had to <u>critisize</u> him for making the <u>metal</u> table <u>unevenly</u>.
            A   B   C

NONE
19. Ⓐ Ⓑ Ⓒ Ⓓ

20. I <u>sympathize</u> for the man who did the <u>unsuccessful</u>
           E   F

<u>magic</u> trick.
 G

NONE
20. Ⓔ Ⓕ Ⓖ Ⓗ

© Macmillan/McGraw-Hill

Name_____

Fold back the paper along the dotted line. Write the words in the blanks as they are read aloud. When you finish the test, unfold the paper. Use the list at the right to correct any spelling mistakes.

1. _____
2. _____
3. _____
4. _____
5. _____
6. _____
7. _____
8. _____
9. _____
10. _____
11. _____
12. _____
13. _____
14. _____
15. _____
16. _____
17. _____
18. _____
19. _____
20. _____

Review Words 21. _____
22. _____
23. _____

Challenge Words 24. _____
25. _____

1. lesson
2. lessen
3. aisle
4. isle
5. I'll
6. navel
7. naval
8. pane
9. pain
10. miner
11. minor
12. vain
13. vane
14. vein
15. principal
16. principle
17. idle
18. idol
19. sheer
20. shear
21. crumble
22. rejection
23. publicity
24. hanger
25. hangar

At Home: Help the student practice the words he or she missed to prepare for the Posttest.

Name_____

Using the Word Study Steps

1. LOOK at the word.

2. SAY the word aloud.

3. STUDY the letters in the word.

4. WRITE the word.

5. CHECK the word.
   Did you spell the word right?
   If not, go back to step 1.

Find the Words

Find and circle the spelling words in the puzzle below.

```
A R P R I N C I P L E B C A
P W L E S S O N A C R E A B
R A V A L M H C A P C E L D
I N A V E I N I J R O K N L
A C L A M N O V A I N O A P
I R E L R O S A I N S O V O
S H E E R R E N ' C T R E N
L U R S I ' L E L I D O L R
E S V S V A R A R P S T E V
L S A E M P P T P A N E A R
E H R N A V A L O L S A L A
V E R E H S I D L E R A H M
I A A A M I N E R R I ' L L
L R O N O L A F E S V R E L
```

At Home: Review the Word Study Steps to help the student spell new words.

Spelling

Homophones: Word Sort

Name_____

lesson	lessen	aisle	isle	I'll
navel	naval	pain	pane	miner
minor	vain	vane	vein	principal
principle	idle	idol	sheer	shear

Sort the spelling words by the number of syllables in each word.

one

1. _____
2. _____
3. _____
4. _____
5. _____
6. _____
7. _____
8. _____

11. _____
12. _____
13. _____
14. _____
15. _____
16. _____
17. _____
18. _____

two

9. _____
10. _____

three

19. _____
20. _____

Write the Words

Use the lines below to practice writing the spelling words.

_____ _____ _____ _____

_____ _____ _____ _____

_____ _____ _____ _____

_____ _____ _____ _____

Name_____

lesson	lessen	aisle	isle	I'll
navel	naval	pain	pane	miner
minor	vain	vane	vein	principal
principle	idle	idol	sheer	shear

Synonyms

Write the spelling word that matches each synonym.

1. chief _____

2. panel _____

3. passageway _____

4. lecture _____

5. hero _____

6. warship _____

7. suffering _____

Antonyms

Write the spelling word that matches each antonym.

8. working _____

9. major _____

10. increase _____

11. humble _____

12. pleasure _____

13. opaque _____

14. artery _____

Name

Proofreading Activity

There are five spelling mistakes in the paragraph below. Circle the misspelled words. Write the words correctly on the line below.

Of all the important people in Zhora's life, her elementary school principle, Mr. Rainer, was one of the most influential. Mr. Reiner taught Zhora one very important lessen in life–the importance of working hard and not being idel. Mr. Reiner explained that life can be difficult and pane is inevitable, but to remain on your goals and persisitently work towards them. Zhora will always rememember Mr. Reiner's poignant words, and considers him her idoll.

1. _____ 2. _____ 3. _____

4. _____ 5. _____

Writing Activity

Is there someone in your life who once gave you some really important advice? Write a letter to that person thanking them for the wisdom they bestowed upon you. Use five spelling words.

_____

_____

_____

_____

_____

_____

_____

_____

_____

Name_____

Look at the words in each set below. One word in each set is spelled correctly. Use a pencil to fill in the circle next to the correct word. Before you begin, look at the sample set of words. Sample A has been done for you. Do Sample B by yourself. When you are sure you know what to do, you may go on with the rest of the page.

Sample A:

Ⓐ hangir
Ⓑ hangurr
Ⓒ hanger
Ⓓ hangerr

Sample B:

Ⓔ hangar
Ⓕ hangarr
Ⓖ handger
Ⓗ hangir

1. Ⓐ lessun
   Ⓑ leson
   Ⓒ lesson
   Ⓓ lescon

6. Ⓔ pane
   Ⓕ pan
   Ⓖ paen
   Ⓗ panne

11. Ⓐ minur
    Ⓑ minier
    Ⓒ minre
    Ⓓ miner

16. Ⓔ lessin
    Ⓕ lessun
    Ⓖ lescen
    Ⓗ lessen

2. Ⓐ asle
   Ⓑ aisel
   Ⓒ aisle
   Ⓓ aell

7. Ⓔ isle
   Ⓕ isel
   Ⓖ isell
   Ⓗ iull

12. Ⓐ naevel
    Ⓑ navull
    Ⓒ naval
    Ⓓ navall

17. Ⓔ minir
    Ⓕ minur
    Ⓖ minor
    Ⓗ minnor

3. Ⓐ vain
   Ⓑ van
   Ⓒ vaen
   Ⓓ vainn

8. Ⓔ van
   Ⓕ vanne
   Ⓖ vaine
   Ⓗ vane

13. Ⓐ principal
    Ⓑ princapil
    Ⓒ prinsipal
    Ⓓ princupal

18. Ⓔ idel
    Ⓕ idal
    Ⓖ idol
    Ⓗ idoll

4. Ⓐ llll
   Ⓑ I'll
   Ⓒ iull
   Ⓓ aull

9. Ⓔ navell
   Ⓕ navull
   Ⓖ navle
   Ⓗ navel

14. Ⓐ idl
    Ⓑ idle
    Ⓒ idel
    Ⓓ idell

19. Ⓔ prinsiple
    Ⓕ princaple
    Ⓖ principle
    Ⓗ principall

5. Ⓐ vien
   Ⓑ veinn
   Ⓒ veine
   Ⓓ vein

10. Ⓔ sher
    Ⓕ shaer
    Ⓖ shear
    Ⓗ sherr

15. Ⓐ pian
    Ⓑ paine
    Ⓒ pan
    Ⓓ pain

20. Ⓔ sher
    Ⓕ shere
    Ⓖ sherr
    Ⓗ sheer

Name_____

Fold back the paper along the dotted line. Write the words in the blanks as they are read aloud. When you finish the test, unfold the paper. Use the list at the right to correct any spelling mistakes.

1. _____
2. _____
3. _____
4. _____
5. _____
6. _____
7. _____
8. _____
9. _____
10. _____
11. _____
12. _____
13. _____
14. _____
15. _____
16. _____
17. _____
18. _____
19. _____
20. _____

Review Words 21. _____
22. _____
23. _____

Challenge Words 24. _____
25. _____

1. aerial
2. aerospace
3. autobiography
4. paragraph
5. biography
6. biology
7. diagram
8. microwave
9. hydrant
10. grammar
11. catalog
12. thermometer
13. microscope
14. microphone
15. chronic
16. program
17. hydrogen
18. dialogue
19. thermos
20. symphony
21. lessen
22. aisle
23. principle
24. graphic
25. logical

At Home: Help the student practice the words he or she missed to prepare for the Posttest.

Name _____

Using the Word Study Steps

1. LOOK at the word.
2. SAY the word aloud.
3. STUDY the letters in the word.
4. WRITE the word.

5. CHECK the word.
Did you spell the word right?
If not, go back to step 1.

Crossword Puzzle

Use the clues to complete the puzzle.

ACROSS

5. When I get older I will write my _____.

6. I keep water in a _____ while I am at the gym.

7. I can't wait to read the new _____ of my favorite singer.

8. I ordered new shoes from a sneaker _____.

9. My doctor used a _____ to take my temperature.

DOWN

1. I enjoyed the orchestra's beautiful rendition of the _____.

2. At the science museum I liked the _____ exhibit.

3. My grandmother has a _____ cough.

4. The fire _____ contains water to fight fires.

5. The photographer took _____ photos while skydiving.

At Home: Review the Word Study Steps to help the student spell new words.

© Macmillan/McGraw-Hill

aerial	aerospace	autobiography	paragraph	biography
biology	diagram	microwave	hydrant	grammar
catalog	thermometer	microscope	microphone	chronic
programs	hydrogen	dialogue	thermos	sympathy

Sort each spelling word according to the Greek root it contains.
Write the words with the following Greek roots:

aer

1. _____

2. _____

bio

3. _____

4. _____

5. _____

chron

6. _____

gram

7. _____

8. _____

9. _____

graph

10. _____

11. _____

12. _____

hydr

13. _____

14. _____

log

15. _____

16. _____

17. _____

micro

18. _____

19. _____

20. _____

phon

21. _____

22. _____

scope

23. _____

Name_____

aerial	aerospace	autobiography	paragraph	biography
biology	diagram	microwave	hydrant	grammar
catalog	thermometer	microscope	microphone	chronic
programs	hydrogen	dialogue	thermos	sympathy

Finish the Set

Write the spelling word that belongs in each group.

1. monologue, conversation, _____

2. chemistry, astronomy, _____

3. oven, toaster, _____

4. word, sentence, _____

5. sandwich bag, lunchbox, _____

6. nitrogen, oxygen, _____

7. atmosphere, outerspace, _____

8. linear or _____ perspective

9. spelling, punctuation,_____

10. slide, specimen, _____

11. kindness, compassion, _____

12. constant, unceasing, _____

13. fire truck, firefighter, fire _____

14. novel, _____, _____

15. drawing, outline, _____

16. radio transmitter, mike, _____

Name_____

Proofreading Activity

There are five spelling mistakes in the paragraph below. Circle the misspelled words. Write the words correctly on the line below.

Mr. Gotay asked each member of his class to write a paragraf about their father. At first, Jimmy was bored with the assignment. His father spent most of his time at work and Jimmy wasn't really sure what he did there. But following his teacher's instruction, he began to ask his father questions about his occupation and other interests. He learned that his father's job was very interesting. He used a microscoop to examine bacteria in an attempt to help cure kronic diseases. Jimmy also learned that his father loved to sing and longed to be on stage with a microfone in his hand. Jimmy decided he would write a biografee about his dad and include all the new and exciting things he learned.

1. _____ 2. _____ 3. _____

4. _____ 5. _____

Writing Activity

Is there something that you have come to appreciate that you did not initially value? Write a short story about a person or experience that allowed you to see the importance of something that you did not originally take note of. Use five spelling words.

_____

_____

_____

_____

_____

_____

Name_____

Look at the words in each set below. One word in each set is
spelled correctly. Use a pencil to fill in the circle next to the correct
word. Before you begin, look at the sample set of words. Sample
A has been done for you. Do Sample B by yourself. When you are
sure you know what to do, you may go on with the rest of the page.

Sample A:

Ⓐ graphik
Ⓑ graphick
Ⓒ graphic
Ⓓ graphec

Sample B:

Ⓔ lojical
Ⓕ logecal
Ⓖ logical
Ⓗ logicall

1. Ⓐ arial
   Ⓑ aerial
   Ⓒ aeriul
   Ⓓ aeriall

2. Ⓐ grammar
   Ⓑ gramar
   Ⓒ grammer
   Ⓓ grammur

3. Ⓐ paragraf
   Ⓑ paragrah
   Ⓒ paragraph
   Ⓓ parugraph

4. Ⓐ khronuc
   Ⓑ cronic
   Ⓒ chronic
   Ⓓ chronuc

5. Ⓐ hidrent
   Ⓑ hydrint
   Ⓒ hydrunt
   Ⓓ hydrant

6. Ⓔ biolojy
   Ⓕ bilogee
   Ⓖ biolowgy
   Ⓗ biology

7. Ⓔ hidrojen
   Ⓕ hydrojen
   Ⓖ hydrogen
   Ⓗ hydrgen

8. Ⓔ thermometer
   Ⓕ thirmomter
   Ⓖ thermometir
   Ⓗ thermomiter

9. Ⓔ digram
   Ⓕ dyagram
   Ⓖ diagrm
   Ⓗ diagram

10. Ⓔ thirmus
    Ⓕ thermoss
    Ⓖ thermos
    Ⓗ thermoss

11. Ⓐ program
    Ⓑ progrum
    Ⓒ progrm
    Ⓓ programm

12. Ⓐ biographee
    Ⓑ biografy
    Ⓒ biography
    Ⓓ biogaphy

13. Ⓐ dyalog
    Ⓑ dialogue
    Ⓒ dialog
    Ⓓ dilogue

14. Ⓐ mykrofone
    Ⓑ microfone
    Ⓒ microphone
    Ⓓ microphon

15. Ⓐ mykroscope
    Ⓑ microskope
    Ⓒ microscope
    Ⓓ mecroscope

16. Ⓔ outobiographee
    Ⓕ autobiography
    Ⓖ autobiographee
    Ⓗ autobigraphy

17. Ⓔ catulog
    Ⓕ catelawg
    Ⓖ catalogg
    Ⓗ catalog

18. Ⓔ erospase
    Ⓕ arospace
    Ⓖ aerospace
    Ⓗ aeruspace

19. Ⓔ mecrowave
    Ⓕ microwave
    Ⓖ microave
    Ⓗ mikrowave

20. Ⓔ symphony
    Ⓕ simfonee
    Ⓖ symfony
    Ⓗ symmphony

Name_____

Fold back the paper along the dotted line. Write the words in the blanks as they are read aloud. When you finish the test, unfold the paper. Use the list at the right to correct any spelling mistakes.

1. _____
2. _____
3. _____
4. _____
5. _____
6. _____
7. _____
8. _____
9. _____
10. _____
11. _____
12. _____
13. _____
14. _____
15. _____
16. _____
17. _____
18. _____
19. _____
20. _____

Review Words 21. _____

22. _____

23. _____

Challenge Words 24. _____

25. _____

1. audience
2. benefit
3. factory
4. flexible
5. reduce
6. credit
7. dictionary
8. section
9. incredible
10. structure
11. insect
12. audio
13. introduce
14. prediction
15. destruction
16. education
17. inject
18. reflection
19. objection
20. dejected
21. biography
22. microphone
23. program
24. manufacture
25. dictate

At Home: Help the student practice the words he or she missed to prepare for the Posttest.

Name_____

Using the Word Study Steps

1. LOOK at the word.
2. SAY the word aloud.
3. STUDY the letters in the word.

4. WRITE the word.
5. CHECK the word.
   Did you spell the word right?
   If not, go back to step 1.

Missing Letters

Fill in the missing letters to form spelling words.

1. pre_____tion

2. struc_____

3. _____dit

4. fac_____

5. educ_____

6. _____ject

7. _____ible

8. dest_____tion

9. _____dio

10. re_____tion

11. ob_____tion

12. ins_____

13. bene_____

14. sec_____

15. de_____ed

16. i_____duce

17. in_____ible

18. re_____e

19. dict_____ary

20. aud_____ce

Make a Puzzle

Make up a puzzle of your own using the space on this page. Give it to someone else to solve. Be sure to include at least five spelling words in your puzzle.

At Home: Review the Word Study Steps to help the student spell new words.

Name_____

audience	benefit	factory	flexible	reduce
credit	dictionary	section	incredible	structure
insect	audio	introduce	prediction	destruction
education	inject	reflection	objection	dejected

**Sort each spelling word according to the Latin root it contains.
Write the words with the following Latin roots:**

aud

1. _____

2. _____

bene

3. _____

cred

4. _____

5. _____

dict

6. _____

7. _____

fac

8. _____

flec/flex

9. _____

10. _____

ject

11. _____

12. _____

13. _____

sect

14. _____

15. _____

Write a Poem

Use the spelling words to write a poem of at least four lines.

_____

_____

_____

_____

Name_____

audience	benefit	factory	flexible	reduce
credit	dictionary	section	incredible	structure
insect	audio	introduce	prediction	destruction
education	inject	reflection	objection	dejected

Sentence Completion

Fill in the blank with the appropriate spelling word.

1. During the wedding nobody made any _____ to the nuptials.

2. My grandmother is diabetic and she has to _____ herself with insulin.

3. In the car we listen to _____ tapes of our favorite musicians.

4. Ms. Nance says we should always look up words we don't know in the

   _____.

5. Hubert works long hard days in the luggage _____.

6. Cody tries to _____ the number of calories he eats when he is on a diet.

7. During the summer my schedule is very _____.

8. In science class we are studying the _____ of genetic material called DNA.

9. Miss Rugpathi asked us to make a _____ about the result of the science experiment.

10. During the baseball game we sat in the _____ closest to the field.

11. During the movie the _____ could not stop laughing.

12. Kristy felt _____ when she did not win the talent show.

13. The town was overwhelmed by the _____ of the tornado.

14. Biologists can learn a lot even if they just study one type of

    _____.

Name_____

Proofreading Activity

There are five spelling mistakes in the paragraph below. Circle the misspelled words. Write the words correctly on the line below.

The hurricane that struck the town of Short Falls left a path of distruction. The local television station hosted an evening to benafit those who had lost so much to the natural disaster. The audance of the program heard many incredable stories that night. There was no objection to a repeat performance of the educashon program.

1. _____   2. _____   3. _____

4. _____   5. _____

Writing Activity

Did your town or neighborhood ever come together for a specific cause? Write a paragraph describing this event. Use five spelling words.

_____
_____
_____
_____
_____
_____
_____
_____
_____
_____
_____

Name_____

Look at the words in each set below. One word in each set is spelled correctly. Use a pencil to fill in the circle next to the correct word. Before you begin, look at the sample set of words. Sample A has been done for you. Do Sample B by yourself. When you are sure you know what to do, you may go on with the rest of the page.

Sample A:

Ⓐ mannufacture
Ⓑ manufactere
Ⓒ manufacture
Ⓓ manufactire

Sample B:

Ⓔ diktate
Ⓕ dicteight
Ⓖ dictate
Ⓗ dictaet

1. Ⓐ benafit
   Ⓑ bennefit
   Ⓒ benefit
   Ⓓ benefitt

2. Ⓐ flexuble
   Ⓑ flexeble
   Ⓒ flexiball
   Ⓓ flexible

3. Ⓐ diktionary
   Ⓑ dictionaree
   Ⓒ dictionary
   Ⓓ dictunary

4. Ⓐ encredable
   Ⓑ incredible
   Ⓒ incrdable
   Ⓓ incredable

5. Ⓐ strukture
   Ⓑ stuckture
   Ⓒ strucktare
   Ⓓ structure

6. Ⓔ prudiction
   Ⓕ predicsion
   Ⓖ predicktion
   Ⓗ prediction

7. Ⓔ reduce
   Ⓕ reduse
   Ⓖ redoose
   Ⓗ redusce

8. Ⓔ educasion
   Ⓕ educashon
   Ⓖ educataation
   Ⓗ education

9. Ⓔ awbjected
   Ⓕ objeckted
   Ⓖ objectid
   Ⓗ objected

10. Ⓔ insect
    Ⓕ ensect
    Ⓖ inseckt
    Ⓗ insekt

11. Ⓐ entroduce
    Ⓑ introduce
    Ⓒ introduse
    Ⓓ introdues

12. Ⓐ kredut
    Ⓑ credet
    Ⓒ credut
    Ⓓ credit

13. Ⓐ inject
    Ⓑ ingect
    Ⓒ injectt
    Ⓓ enject

14. Ⓐ cektion
    Ⓑ secktion
    Ⓒ section
    Ⓓ secshion

15. Ⓐ degectid
    Ⓑ dejected
    Ⓒ dejektid
    Ⓓ dejekted

16. Ⓔ factoree
    Ⓕ factory
    Ⓖ factary
    Ⓗ factry

17. Ⓔ destruction
    Ⓕ distruksion
    Ⓖ destrucsion
    Ⓗ dastrction

18. Ⓔ awdience
    Ⓕ audiennce
    Ⓖ audience
    Ⓗ audewnce

19. Ⓔ reflection
    Ⓕ reefletion
    Ⓖ reflecshion
    Ⓗ reflecsion

20. Ⓔ awdio
    Ⓕ audeo
    Ⓖ audio
    Ⓗ audo

Name_____

Fold back the paper along the dotted line. Write the words in the blanks as they are read aloud. When you finish the test, unfold the paper. Use the list at the right to correct any spelling mistakes.

1. _____
2. _____
3. _____
4. _____
5. _____
6. _____
7. _____
8. _____
9. _____
10. _____
11. _____
12. _____
13. _____
14. _____
15. _____
16. _____
17. _____
18. _____
19. _____
20. _____

Review Words 21. _____

22. _____

23. _____

Challenge Words 24. _____

25. _____

1. terrible
2. impossible
3. valuable
4. noticeable
5. considerable
6. available
7. horrible
8. believable
9. audible
10. predictable
11. remarkable
12. reversible
13. changeable
14. reliable
15. acceptable
16. probable
17. admirable
18. dependable
19. profitable
20. lovable
21. credit
22. dictionary
23. education
24. eligible
25. legible

© Macmillan/McGraw-Hill

At Home: Help the student practice the words he or she missed to prepare for the Posttest.

Name_____

Using the Word Study Steps

1. LOOK at the word.

2. SAY the word aloud.

3. STUDY the letters in the word.

4. WRITE the word.

5. CHECK the word.
   Did you spell the word right?
   If not, go back to step 1.

Find the Words

**Find and circle the spelling words hidden in each set of letters.
Then write them on the line.**

1. d e p e n o t i c e a b l e _____

2. b e l i b e l i e v a b l e _____

3. t e r r e l i a b l e i b l e _____

4. a v a i m p o s s i b l e _____

5. l o v a b l e p e n d a b l e _____

6. a l w p r o v i t a v a i l a b l e _____

7. p r e d i c t a b l e i e a b l e _____

8. n o t i c a c c e p t a b l e _____

9. c o n s i d e r a b l e b b l e _____

10. p r e r e v e r e m a r k a b l e _____

11. c o n r e v a l u a b l e i b l e _____

12. h o r r i b c h a n g e a b l e _____

13. r e l i a d m i r a b l e i b l e _____

14. p r e p r o b a b l e r a t i o n _____

15. p r e d e p e n d a b l e i b l e _____

 At Home: Review the Word Study Steps to help the student
spell new words.

Name_____

terrible	impossible	valuable	noticeable	considerable
available	horrible	believable	audible	predictable
remarkable	reversible	changeable	reliable	acceptable
probable	admirable	dependable	profitable	lovable

Sort the spelling words according to their suffix.

-able

1. _____
2. _____
3. _____
4. _____
5. _____
6. _____
7. _____
8. _____
9. _____
10. _____
11. _____
12. _____
13. _____
14. _____
15. _____

-ible

16. _____
17. _____
18. _____
19. _____
20. _____

Name_____

terrible	impossible	valuable	noticeable	considerable
available	horrible	believable	audible	predictable
remarkable	reversible	changeable	reliable	acceptable
probable	admirable	dependable	profitable	lovable

Matching Meanings

Write the spelling word that matches each definition.

1. extraordinary   _____

2. expensive   _____

3. splendid   _____

4. suitable   _____

5. substantial   _____

6. endearing   _____

7. obvious   _____

8. lucrative   _____

9. likely   _____

10. expected   _____

11. plausible   _____

12. ready   _____

13. variable   _____

Synonyms

**Choose another spelling word that is synonymous with the
spelling words listed below.**

14. reliable   _____

15. horrible   _____

© Macmillan/McGraw-Hill

Name_____

Proofreading Activity

There are five spelling mistakes in the paragraph below. Circle the misspelled words. Write the words correctly on the line below.

Sidney Quinn has a remarkible collection of miniature automobiles. Sidney has been collecting cars for a considerible amount of time—nearly eighty years. He always gets excited when a new miniature car model becomes avalable. His collection has proved to be very profatabell, as some of his cars are incredibly valueable. But Sidney does not collect for the money he makes, he collects because he loves his miniature automobiles.

1. _____   2. _____   3. _____

4. _____   5. _____

Writing Activity

Do you have any collections? Write a paragraph describing something you collect. Use at least five spelling words.

_____

_____

_____

_____

_____

_____

_____

_____

_____

_____

Name_____

Look at the words in each set below. One word in each set is spelled correctly. Use a pencil to fill in the circle next to the correct word. Before you begin, look at the sample set of words. Sample A has been done for you. Do Sample B by yourself. When you are sure you know what to do, you may go on with the rest of the page.

Sample A:

Ⓐ elligable
Ⓑ eligibell
Ⓒ eligible
Ⓓ eligable

Sample B:

Ⓔ legable
Ⓕ legabell
Ⓖ legible
Ⓗ legibell

1. Ⓐ konsiderable
   Ⓑ considerable
   Ⓒ conciderable
   Ⓓ considerabell

2. Ⓐ reversable
   Ⓑ reversibell
   Ⓒ reverrsible
   Ⓓ reversible

3. Ⓐ awdible
   Ⓑ auidbell
   Ⓒ audable
   Ⓓ audible

4. Ⓐ valuable
   Ⓑ valuble
   Ⓒ valueable
   Ⓓ valuabell

5. Ⓐ horible
   Ⓑ horribell
   Ⓒ horribull
   Ⓓ horrible

6. Ⓔ lovable
   Ⓕ loveable
   Ⓖ lovabell
   Ⓗ lovabl

7. Ⓔ terribell
   Ⓕ terruble
   Ⓖ terrible
   Ⓗ terible

8. Ⓔ acceptable
   Ⓕ aceptable
   Ⓖ acceptible
   Ⓗ acceptabell

9. Ⓔ probabell
   Ⓕ probubel
   Ⓖ probabl
   Ⓗ probable

10. Ⓔ dependabell
    Ⓕ dependbull
    Ⓖ dependable
    Ⓗ dependeble

11. Ⓐ remarkable
    Ⓑ remarkabell
    Ⓒ remarckabell
    Ⓓ remmarkable

12. Ⓐ changable
    Ⓑ changeable
    Ⓒ changebell
    Ⓓ changabell

13. Ⓐ avalable
    Ⓑ available
    Ⓒ avialabell
    Ⓓ aavailable

14. Ⓐ admirable
    Ⓑ admirubell
    Ⓒ admiroble
    Ⓓ admireble

15. Ⓐ profitable
    Ⓑ profituble
    Ⓒ profittable
    Ⓓ profitabell

16. Ⓔ immposible
    Ⓕ impossible
    Ⓖ imposable
    Ⓗ impossebell

17. Ⓔ believable
    Ⓕ beeleevable
    Ⓖ beleivable
    Ⓗ believeable

18. Ⓔ reeliable
    Ⓕ reliabell
    Ⓖ reliabel
    Ⓗ reliable

19. Ⓔ noticable
    Ⓕ noticeuble
    Ⓖ noticeable
    Ⓗ noticabell

20. Ⓔ predictabell
    Ⓕ predictable
    Ⓖ predicteble
    Ⓗ pridictable

© Macmillan/McGraw-Hill

Name_____

Fold back the paper along the dotted line. Write the words in the blanks as they are read aloud. When you finish the test, unfold the paper. Use the list at the right to correct any spelling mistakes.

1. _____
2. _____
3. _____
4. _____
5. _____
6. _____
7. _____
8. _____
9. _____
10. _____
11. _____
12. _____
13. _____
14. _____
15. _____
16. _____
17. _____
18. _____
19. _____
20. _____

Review Words 21. _____
22. _____
23. _____

Challenge Words 24. _____
25. _____

1. experience
2. evident
3. persistent
4. intelligent
5. defiance
6. constant
7. violence
8. permanent
9. president
10. incident
11. important
12. excellent
13. fragrance
14. acquaintance
15. conference
16. disappearance
17. occurence
18. nuisance
19. observant
20. hesitant
21. terrible
22. noticeable
23. profitable
24. elegance
25. diligent

© Macmillan/McGraw-Hill

At Home: Help the student practice the words he or she missed to prepare for the Posttest.

Name_____

Using the Word Study Steps

1. LOOK at the word.

2. SAY the word aloud.

3. STUDY the letters in the word.

4. WRITE the word.

5. CHECK the word.
Did you spell the word right?
If not, go back to step 1.

Missing Vowels

Fill in the missing vowels to form spelling words.

1. pr __ s __ d __

2. d __ s __ pp __ __ r __ nc __

3. p __ rs __ st __ nt

4. __ xc __ ll __ nt

5. d __ f __ __ nc __

6. __ xp __ r __ __ nc __

7. c __ nf __ r __ nce

8. __ bs __ rv __ nt

9. __ mp __ rt __ nt

10. v __ __ l __ nc __

11. h __ s __ t __ nt

12. __ v __ d __ nt

13. c __ nst __ nt

14. __ nc __ d __ nt

15. __ nt __ ll __ g __ nt

16. __ cq __ __ __ nt __ nc __

17. p __ rm __ n __ nt

18. n __ __ s __ nc __

19. fr __ gr __ nc __

20. __ cc __ rr __ nc __

Write the Words

Use the lines below to practice writing the spelling words.

_____ _____ _____ _____

_____ _____ _____ _____

_____ _____ _____ _____

_____ _____ _____ _____

At Home: Review the Word Study Steps to help the student spell new words.

© Macmillan/McGraw-Hill

experience	evident	persistent	intelligent	defiance
constant	violence	permanent	president	incident
important	excellent	fragrance	acquaintance	conference
disappearance	occurrence	nuisance	observant	hesitant

Sort the spelling words according to their suffixes.

-ant

1. _____
2. _____
3. _____
4. _____

-ent

5. _____
6. _____
7. _____
8. _____
9. _____
10. _____
11. _____

-ance

12. _____
13. _____
14. _____
15. _____
16. _____

-ence

17. _____
18. _____
19. _____
20. _____

Write About It

Use one of the sets of words above in a short piece of writing
about a topic of your choice.

_____

_____

_____

Name_____

experience	evident	persistent	intelligent	defiance
constant	violence	permanent	president	incident
important	excellent	fragrance	acquaintance	conference
disappearance	occurrence	nuisance	observant	hesitant

Word Meanings

Write the spelling word that matches each definition.

1. paying careful attention to _____

2. a meeting _____

3. the person who holds the head position _____

4. a person who is less known than a friend _____

5. a pleasant smell _____

6. of a very high quality or standard _____

7. refusal to conform _____

8. activity or events that in time increase skill _____

9. a person or thing that is annoying _____

10. lasting forever _____

11. showing high levels of thought _____

12. having significant value _____

13. no longer being seen _____

14. reluctance to say or do something _____

15. use of physical force to damage _____

16. unchanging, invariable _____

17. clear to the vision or understanding _____

18. existing for a longer time; continuously _____

Proofreading Activity

There are five spelling mistakes in the paragraph below. Circle the misspelled words. Write the words correctly on the line below.

Last summer the town pool passed a rule that no child under twelve could swim without a parent present. They decided to pass this rule following an insident involving a ten year-old boy who was a newsance to the swimmers and sunbathers. He never caused any vilance but everyone was annoyed with him. Due to that one boy the pool board decided to close the pool to everyone under twelve who didn't have a parent to look after them. My friends and I decided to stand up for ourselves. We wrote the pool board a letter explaining how emportant the pool was to us and what a great expeeriance it was for us to enjoy the pool with the other residents in our town. I guess our argument was persuasive. Three days after the new rule went into effect it was overturned.

1. _____ 2. _____ 3. _____

4. _____ 5. _____

Writing Activity

Don't you feel great when you stand up for something you believe in? Write a short story in which you stood up for something you really wanted and your efforts paid off. Use at least five spelling words.

_____

_____

_____

_____

_____

_____

_____

Name_____

Look at the words in each set below. One word in each set is
spelled correctly. Use a pencil to fill in the circle next to the correct
word. Before you begin, look at the sample set of words. Sample
A has been done for you. Do Sample B by yourself. When you are
sure you know what to do, you may go on with the rest of the page.

Sample A:

Ⓐ ellegance
Ⓑ ellagance
Ⓒ elegance
Ⓓ elagence

Sample B:

Ⓔ dillijent
Ⓕ diligent
Ⓖ dilligent
Ⓗ dilignt

1. Ⓐ ixperience
   Ⓑ expirience
   Ⓒ experrience
   Ⓓ experience

6. Ⓔ fragrance
   Ⓕ fragrunce
   Ⓖ fragranc
   Ⓗ fragranss

11. Ⓐ ivident
    Ⓑ evident
    Ⓒ evidennt
    Ⓓ evadent

16. Ⓔ akquaintance
    Ⓕ acquantence
    Ⓖ acquaintance
    Ⓗ acquintence

2. Ⓐ pirsistent
   Ⓑ pirsistunt
   Ⓒ percistent
   Ⓓ persistent

7. Ⓔ permanent
   Ⓕ pirmanent
   Ⓖ permanint
   Ⓗ perrmanent

12. Ⓐ prezidnet
    Ⓑ presudent
    Ⓒ presedent
    Ⓓ president

17. Ⓔ entilligent
    Ⓕ intelligent
    Ⓖ intellijent
    Ⓗ intelligant

3. Ⓐ difince
   Ⓑ defianse
   Ⓒ defiance
   Ⓓ defianss

8. Ⓔ encedent
   Ⓕ incedent
   Ⓖ incident
   Ⓗ incadent

13. Ⓐ excillent
    Ⓑ excellent
    Ⓒ excelent
    Ⓓ excallent

18. Ⓔ important
    Ⓕ importint
    Ⓖ immmportant
    Ⓗ importunt

4. Ⓐ conference
   Ⓑ confrence
   Ⓒ konference
   Ⓓ konfrunce

9. Ⓔ dissapearance
   Ⓕ disappearanse
   Ⓖ disappearance
   Ⓗ dissappearance

14. Ⓐ accurence
    Ⓑ occurrance
    Ⓒ occurrence
    Ⓓ ockurrence

19. Ⓔ konstant
    Ⓕ constant
    Ⓖ constent
    Ⓗ connstant

5. Ⓐ violense
   Ⓑ vilince
   Ⓒ violance
   Ⓓ violence

10. Ⓔ nuisance
    Ⓕ newsance
    Ⓖ nusance
    Ⓗ nuisanse

15. Ⓐ obbservant
    Ⓑ obsirvant
    Ⓒ observint
    Ⓓ observant

20. Ⓔ hezitant
    Ⓕ hesitunt
    Ⓖ hesitant
    Ⓗ hesutant

© Macmillan/McGraw-Hill

Name_____

Read each sentence. If an underlined word is spelled wrong, fill in the circle that goes with that word. If no word is spelled wrong, fill in the circle below NONE. Read Sample A and do Sample B.

A. It is <u>importent</u> for a <u>president</u> to be <u>intelligent</u>.
  A   B   C

NONE
A. Ⓐ Ⓑ Ⓒ Ⓓ

B. The <u>biography</u> I am reading is so <u>remarkable</u>, it is
       E   F

barely <u>believeable</u>.
      G

NONE
B. Ⓔ Ⓕ Ⓖ Ⓗ

1. It is a great <u>benefit</u> to own a <u>relieable</u> <u>dictionary</u>.
        A   B   C

NONE
1. Ⓐ Ⓑ Ⓒ Ⓓ

2. Andre's weather <u>vane</u> was so <u>notisable</u> that his
            E   F

neighbors took an <u>objection</u> to it.
         G

NONE
2. Ⓔ Ⓕ Ⓖ Ⓗ

3. The singer was barely <u>audible</u> to the <u>audience</u> and
           A   B

needed a <u>microphon</u>.
       C

NONE
3. Ⓐ Ⓑ Ⓒ Ⓓ

4. The doctor looked through the medical <u>catalog</u> when he
                   E

wanted to purchase a new <u>microscope</u> and <u>thermometer</u>.
           F   G

NONE
4. Ⓔ Ⓕ Ⓖ Ⓗ

5. Mrs. Briggs felt that her <u>lesson</u> on <u>grammer</u> was a very
           A   B

<u>valuable</u> one.
    C

NONE
5. Ⓐ Ⓑ Ⓒ Ⓓ

6. The <u>miner</u> was angered by the <u>horribal</u> <u>occurrence</u> of
     E   F   G

bad weather.

NONE
6. Ⓔ Ⓕ Ⓖ Ⓗ

7. When I developed the <u>excellent</u> <u>fragrance</u> I gave it to
           A   B

an <u>acquaintance</u>.
     C

NONE
7. Ⓐ Ⓑ Ⓒ Ⓓ

8. The diagram shows an arial view of the factory.
       E   F   G

                                                    NONE
        8. Ⓔ Ⓕ Ⓖ Ⓗ

                                                    NONE

9. A permanant police officer was placed on duty in an
     A

   attempt to reduce violence.
             B   C

        9. Ⓐ Ⓑ Ⓒ Ⓓ

                                                    NONE

10. His chronic cough caused him to experiance pain.
        E   F   G

      10. Ⓔ Ⓕ Ⓖ Ⓗ

                                                    NONE

11. My reflection was in the glass pane on the microwave.
          A   B   C

      11. Ⓐ Ⓑ Ⓒ Ⓓ

                                                    NONE

12. I knelt in the aisal to make an audio of the symphony.
                  E   F   G

      12. Ⓔ Ⓕ Ⓖ Ⓗ

                                                    NONE

13. In biology you can learn if there is any hidrogen in a vein.
        A   B   C

      13. Ⓐ Ⓑ Ⓒ Ⓓ

                                                    NONE

14. A dependable search party was sent in response to
        E

    the disappearance of the miner.
          F   G

      14. Ⓔ Ⓕ Ⓖ Ⓗ

                                                    NONE

15. I'll write the rest of my autobiography someday. I've
    A   B

    just written the first paragraf.
                           C

      15. Ⓐ Ⓑ Ⓒ Ⓓ

                                                    NONE

16. The insect is a newsance to that factory.
              E   F   G

      16. Ⓔ Ⓕ Ⓖ Ⓗ

                                                    NONE

17. The doctor has to injekt the available medicine directly
                           A   B

    into my vein.
             C

      17. Ⓐ Ⓑ Ⓒ Ⓓ

                                                    NONE

18. My principal is my idol because he is so admirable.
          E   F   G

      18. Ⓔ Ⓕ Ⓖ Ⓗ

                                                    NONE

19. Caitlin was very observant during the incredible conference.
                            A   B   C

      19. Ⓐ Ⓑ Ⓒ Ⓓ

                                                    NONE

20. Should I focus my education on naval or airospace studies.
                              E   F   G

      20. Ⓔ Ⓕ Ⓖ Ⓗ

© Macmillan/McGraw-Hill

Name _____

Fold back the paper along the dotted line. Write the words in the blanks as they are read aloud. When you finish the test, unfold the paper. Use the list at the right to correct any spelling mistakes.

1. _____ 1. co-worker
2. _____ 2. commission
3. _____ 3. transformation
4. _____ 4. proportion
5. _____ 5. cooperate
6. _____ 6. intersection
7. _____ 7. profession
8. _____ 8. transparent
9. _____ 9. submit
10. _____ 10. interrupt
11. _____ 11. postpone
12. _____ 12. companion
13. _____ 13. submarine
14. _____ 14. postwar
15. _____ 15. transform
16. _____ 16. suburb
17. _____ 17. combine
18. _____ 18. interfere
19. _____ 19. transfer
20. _____ 20. copilot

Review Words
21. _____ 21. experience
22. _____ 22. intelligent
23. _____ 23. persistent

Challenge Words
24. _____ 24. profound
25. _____ 25. subscribe

At Home: Help the student practice the words he or she missed to prepare for the Posttest.

Using the Word Study Steps

1. LOOK at the word.

2. SAY the word aloud.

3. STUDY the letters in the word.

4. WRITE the word.

5. CHECK the word.
   Did you spell the word right?
   If not, go back to step 1.

Find Rhyming Words

Circle the word in each row that does not rhyme with the spelling
word on the left.

1. interfere	cavalry	volunteer	pioneer
2. transform	reform	storm	alarm
3. interrupt	abrupt	corrupt	script
4. profession	admission	obsession	discretion
5. proportion	distortion	emotion	contortion
6. postwar	beware	décor	explore
7. transfer	prefer	confer	laughter
8. submit	transmit	allot	permit
9. commission	contortion	tradition	ambition
10. submarine	routine	shine	caffeine
11. combine	assign	decline	fringe
12. transparent	clearance	parent	apparent
13. intersection	direction	temptation	perfection
14. postpone	cyclone	alone	crown
15. transportation	vacation	selection	sensation

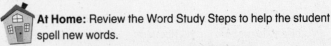 **At Home:** Review the Word Study Steps to help the student
spell new words.

© Macmillan/McGraw-Hill

Name _____

co-worker	commission	transformation	proportion	cooperate
intersection	profession	transparent	submit	interrupt
postpone	companion	submarine	postwar	transform
suburb	combine	interfere	transfer	copilot

Sort the spelling words by their prefix.

co-

1. _____
2. _____
3. _____

com-

4. _____
5. _____
6. _____

inter-

7. _____
8. _____
9. _____

post-

10. _____
11. _____

pro-

12. _____
13. _____

sub-

14. _____
15. _____
16. _____

trans-

17. _____
18. _____
19. _____
20. _____

Name_____

co-worker	commission	transformation	proportion	cooperate
intersection	profession	transparent	submit	interrupt
postpone	companion	submarine	postwar	transform
suburb	combine	interfere	transfer	copilot

Matching Meanings

Write the spelling word that matches each definition.

1. impede _____

2. delay _____

3. assist _____

4. disturb _____

5. associate _____

6. community _____

7. crossroads _____

8. relocate _____

9. payment _____

10. friend _____

11. move _____

12. ratio _____

13. mix _____

14. occupation _____

15. alter _____

16. hand in _____

17. diving equipment _____

18. obvious; clear _____

© Macmillan/McGraw-Hill

Name_____

There are five spelling mistakes in the paragraph below. Circle the misspelled words. Write the words correctly on the lines below.

Each year the Martin Luther King Jr. Middle School holds a design competition. Imani and her companyon Bartholomew decided to work together for the competition. They wanted to design a playground for their community in a suberb of New York City. They knew if they could coperate and comebine their talents they would have a good chance of winning. They were eager to submitt their design. They were even happier to find out that they had won.

1. _____   2. _____   3. _____

4. _____   5. _____

Writing Activity

Were you ever really excited to find out that you had won something? Write a letter to a friend explaining how you felt after you had won. Use five spelling words.

_____

_____

_____

_____

_____

_____

_____

_____

_____

_____

Name＿＿＿＿＿＿＿＿＿＿＿＿＿＿＿＿＿＿＿＿＿＿＿

Look at the words in each set below. One word in each set is spelled correctly. Use a pencil to fill in the circle next to the correct word. Before you begin, look at the sample set of words. Sample A has been done for you. Do Sample B by yourself. When you are sure you know what to do, you may go on with the rest of the page.

Sample A:

Ⓐ profund
Ⓑ profownd
Ⓒ profound
Ⓓ proffound

Sample B:

Ⓔ subskribe
Ⓕ subsckribe
Ⓖ subscribe
Ⓗ subbscribe

1. Ⓐ cooworker
   Ⓑ ko-worker
   Ⓒ co-worker
   Ⓓ co-worcker

2. Ⓔ subburb
   Ⓕ suberb
   Ⓖ suburb
   Ⓗ subirb

3. Ⓐ proporttion
   Ⓑ proporzion
   Ⓒ proportion
   Ⓓ proporstion

4. Ⓔ profession
   Ⓕ profesion
   Ⓖ proffesion
   Ⓗ profeszion

5. Ⓐ kooperate
   Ⓑ coopireight
   Ⓒ cooperate
   Ⓓ cooperrate

6. Ⓔ submitt
   Ⓕ submit
   Ⓖ submmitt
   Ⓗ subbmit

7. Ⓐ transform
   Ⓑ transformm
   Ⓒ transferm
   Ⓓ tranzform

8. Ⓔ enterfere
   Ⓕ interrfere
   Ⓖ interfear
   Ⓗ interfere

9. Ⓐ kompanion
   Ⓑ compainon
   Ⓒ compaineon
   Ⓓ companion

10. Ⓔ transfer
    Ⓕ tranzfer
    Ⓖ transfir
    Ⓗ transsfer

11. Ⓐ kopilot
    Ⓑ copielut
    Ⓒ copilet
    Ⓓ copilot

12. Ⓔ cummision
    Ⓕ commision
    Ⓖ commizion
    Ⓗ commission

13. Ⓐ posspone
    Ⓑ postpone
    Ⓒ postpon
    Ⓓ postpoen

14. Ⓔ subbmarine
    Ⓕ submareen
    Ⓖ submarine
    Ⓗ submarene

15. Ⓐ postwir
    Ⓑ postwar
    Ⓒ postwr
    Ⓓ postwarr

16. Ⓔ intersection
    Ⓕ entersection
    Ⓖ intersesion
    Ⓗ intersecshon

17. Ⓐ interrupt
    Ⓑ interupt
    Ⓒ enterrupt
    Ⓓ inturupt

18. Ⓔ combine
    Ⓕ combene
    Ⓖ combien
    Ⓗ commbine

19. Ⓐ tranzformasion
    Ⓑ transformation
    Ⓒ transsformation
    Ⓓ transformazion

20. Ⓔ tranzparent
    Ⓕ transparint
    Ⓖ transsparent
    Ⓗ transparent

Name_____

Fold back the paper along the dotted line. Write the words in the blanks as they are read aloud. When you finish the test, unfold the paper. Use the list at the right to correct any spelling mistakes.

1. _____
2. _____
3. _____
4. _____
5. _____
6. _____
7. _____
8. _____
9. _____
10. _____
11. _____
12. _____
13. _____
14. _____
15. _____
16. _____
17. _____
18. _____
19. _____
20. _____

Review Words 21. _____
22. _____
23. _____
Challenge Words 24. _____
25. _____

1. immigrate
2. impatiently
3. accompany
4. announce
5. arrive
6. collect
7. arrest
8. irregular
9. illuminate
10. accomodate
11. collaborate
12. immature
13. suffix
14. illogical
15. immigration
16. suppress
17. illegal
18. support
19. correspond
20. assembly
21. cooperate
22. profession
23. suburb
24. impractical
25. suffocate

At Home: Help the student practice the words he or she missed to prepare for the Posttest.

Name _____

Using the Word Study Steps

1. LOOK at the word.

2. SAY the word aloud.

3. STUDY the letters in the word.

4. WRITE the word.

5. CHECK the word.
   Did you spell the word right?
   If not, go back to step 1.

Find the Words

Find and circle the spelling words in the puzzle below.

```
I  L  L  O  G  I  C  A  L  A  C  C  O  M
D  A  S  S  E  M  B  L  Y  F  P  E  G  R
R  I  U  P  I  M  A  N  N  O  U  N  C  E
I  M  P  A  T  I  E  N  T  L  Y  A  C  I
M  M  P  C  O  G  A  H  A  J  I  G  O  L
M  A  R  C  A  R  R  E  S  T  L  I  L  L
I  T  E  O  B  A  R  R  U  S  L  R  L  U
G  U  S  M  C  T  I  X  P  A  E  R  A  M
R  R  S  P  O  E  V  P  P  R  G  E  B  I
A  E  H  A  L  H  E  N  O  A  A  G  O  N
T  P  R  N  L  L  D  S  R  E  L  U  R  A
I  D  E  Y  E  I  H  I  T  H  K  L  A  T
O  N  M  A  C  C  O  M  M  O  D  A  T  E
N  I  X  H  T  S  U  F  F  I  X  R  E  C
C  O  R  R  E  S  P  O  N  D  L  E  K  Y
```

At Home: Review the Word Study Steps to help the student spell new words.

© Macmillan/McGraw-Hill

immigrate	impatiently	accompany	announce	arrive
collect	arrest	irregular	illuminate	accommodate
collaborate	immature	suffix	illogical	immigration
suppress	illegal	support	correspond	assembly

Sort the spelling words by their prefix.

a-

1. _____
2. _____
3. _____
4. _____
5. _____
6. _____

co-

7. _____
8. _____
9. _____

il-

10. _____
11. _____
12. _____

im-

13. _____
14. _____
15. _____
16. _____

ir-

17. _____

su-

18. _____
19. _____
20. _____

Name_____

immigrate	impatiently	accompany	announce	arrive
collect	arrest	irregular	illuminate	accommodate
collaborate	immature	suffix	illogical	immigration
suppress	illegal	support	correspond	assembly

Synonyms

Write the spelling word that matches each synonym.

1. proclaim _____

2. childish _____

3. aid _____

4. gather _____

5. meeting _____

6. escort _____

Antonyms

Write the spelling word that matches each antonym.

7. release _____

8. reasonable _____

9. authorized _____

10. express _____

11. darken _____

12. leave _____

Name_____

There are five spelling mistakes in the paragraph below. Circle the misspelled words. Write the words correctly on the lines below.

Salvatore often imagined what it would be like to travel to another time. His family had moved from Italy to New York when he was ten. He imagined that living in another century would be similar to how he felt when his family decided to emmigrate. He supposed the immigrasion process would be much more difficult if you traveled back in time to the eighteenth century. Salvatore guessed that if he were to arive back then things would seem more irreguler and ilogical than when he moved from Italy.

1. _____   2. _____   3. _____

4. _____   5. _____

Writing Activity

Did you ever fantasize about time travel? Imagine that you have traveled back in time. Write a letter to a friend describing your experience. Use at least five spelling words.

_____

_____

_____

_____

_____

_____

_____

_____

_____

_____

Name_____

Look at the words in each set below. One word in each set is spelled correctly. Use a pencil to fill in the circle next to the correct word. Before you begin, look at the sample set of words. Sample A has been done for you. Do Sample B by yourself. When you are sure you know what to do, you may go on with the rest of the page.

Sample A:

Ⓐ kooperate
Ⓑ coperate
Ⓒ cooperate
Ⓓ coopereight

Sample B:

Ⓔ proffession
Ⓕ profeshon
Ⓖ profession
Ⓗ profesion

1. Ⓐ imigrate
    Ⓑ emmigrate
    Ⓒ emigrate
    Ⓓ immigrate

2. Ⓔ ackompany
    Ⓕ accompany
    Ⓖ akcompany
    Ⓗ accompeny

3. Ⓐ accommodate
    Ⓑ ackomodate
    Ⓒ accumadate
    Ⓓ akommodate

4. Ⓔ arest
    Ⓕ arrest
    Ⓖ urrest
    Ⓗ arresst

5. Ⓐ imature
    Ⓑ emmature
    Ⓒ immature
    Ⓓ immattir

6. Ⓔ illogical
    Ⓕ ilogical
    Ⓖ ellogical
    Ⓗ elogical

7. Ⓐ anounce
    Ⓑ annonce
    Ⓒ unnounce
    Ⓓ announce

8. Ⓔ suport
    Ⓕ suppert
    Ⓖ support
    Ⓗ supportt

9. Ⓐ supres
    Ⓑ suppres
    Ⓒ suppress
    Ⓓ supress

10. Ⓔ iluminate
    Ⓕ elluminate
    Ⓖ illumminate
    Ⓗ illuminate

11. Ⓐ sufix
    Ⓑ suffix
    Ⓒ cuffix
    Ⓓ suffex

12. Ⓔ arrive
    Ⓕ arive
    Ⓖ arivve
    Ⓗ urrive

13. Ⓐ corespond
    Ⓑ correspond
    Ⓒ correspnd
    Ⓓ corrispond

14. Ⓔ ilegal
    Ⓕ ellegal
    Ⓖ illegal
    Ⓗ illegall

15. Ⓐ asembly
    Ⓑ assemmbly
    Ⓒ asemmbly
    Ⓓ assembly

16. Ⓔ empatiently
    Ⓕ impationetly
    Ⓖ impatiently
    Ⓗ impashontly

17. Ⓐ erregular
    Ⓑ iregular
    Ⓒ irregulir
    Ⓓ irregular

18. Ⓔ colabrate
    Ⓕ kollaborate
    Ⓖ cullaborate
    Ⓗ collaborate

19. Ⓐ immigration
    Ⓑ imigration
    Ⓒ emmigration
    Ⓓ immigrashion

20. Ⓔ collect
    Ⓕ kollect
    Ⓖ colect
    Ⓗ collectt

© Macmillan/McGraw-Hill

Name_____

Fold back the paper along the dotted line. Write the words in the blanks as they are read aloud. When you finish the test, unfold the paper. Use the list at the right to correct any spelling mistakes.

1. _____
2. _____
3. _____
4. _____
5. _____
6. _____
7. _____
8. _____
9. _____
10. _____
11. _____
12. _____
13. _____
14. _____
15. _____
16. _____
17. _____
18. _____
19. _____
20. _____

Review Words 21. _____
22. _____
23. _____

Challenge Words 24. _____
25. _____

1. democrat
2. democracy
3. physician
4. zoology
5. telepathy
6. sympathy
7. technology
8. biologist
9. pianist
10. geologist
11. musician
12. ecology
13. apology
14. politician
15. tourist
16. heroism
17. technician
18. novelist
19. archaeology
20. specialist
21. announce
22. collect
23. illegal
24. electrician
25. mythology

© Macmillan/McGraw-Hill

At Home: Help the student practice the words he or she missed to prepare for the Posttest.

Name _____

Using the Word Study Steps

1. LOOK at the word.

2. SAY the word aloud.

3. STUDY the letters in the word.

4. WRITE the word.

5. CHECK the word.
   Did you spell the word right?
   If not, go back to step 1.

ACROSS

1. a piano player

5. a doctor

6. advances in tools and
   knowledge

7. a person who creates
   music

DOWN

1. a person who participates
   in politics

2. a person who visits a
   place far from their home

3. communication of the
   minds

4. a person who is particularly
   knowledgeable in a specific
   field

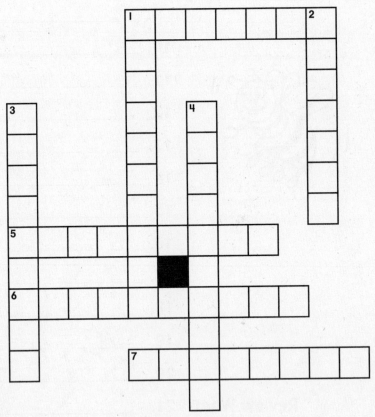

At Home: Review the Word Study Steps to help the student
spell new words.

© Macmillan/McGraw-Hill

Name _____

democrat   democracy   physician   zoology   telepathy
sympathy   technology   biologist   pianist   geologist
musician   ecology   apology   politician   tourist
heroism   technician   novelist   archaeology   specialist

Sort the spelling words by their suffix.

-crat/-cracy

1. _____
2. _____

-ician

3. _____
4. _____
5. _____
6. _____

-ism/-ist

7. _____
8. _____
9. _____
10. _____
11. _____

-logy/-logist

12. _____
13. _____
14. _____
15. _____
16. _____
17. _____
18. _____

-pathy

19. _____
20. _____

Name_____

democrat	democracy	physician	zoology	telepathy
sympathy	technology	biologist	pianist	geologist
musician	ecology	apology	politician	tourist
heroism	technician	novelist	archaeology	specialist

Sentence Completion

Fill in the blank with the appropriate spelling word.

1. After a week of stomach pains, Lenore decided to consult a

   _____.

2. Mike's _____ wasn't enough to make her feel better.

3. Denise wants to be a _____ because she loves to study
   plants and animals.

4. Antonia is very interested in animals and is considering studying

   _____.

5. Farhad likes _____, the study of ancient cultures.

6. When Duke's turtle died I sent him a _____ card.

7. Ashley is a republican, but her sister is a _____.

8. The cable company sent a _____ to install our television.

9. He was a world renown _____ in gemology.

10. Lance takes guitar lessons and dreams of becoming a famous

    _____.

11. Mo and Beau are such good friends they always know what the other is

    thinking; its like they have mental _____.

12. Drew is working on a book and hopes to be a professional

    _____.

13. We studied _____ in our environmental science class.

14. Computer _____ has grown substantially in the past ten years.

© Macmillan/McGraw-Hill

Name _____

There are five spelling mistakes in the paragraph below. Circle the misspelled words. Write the words correctly on the lines below.

     If there is one profession I most want to be it is a polititian. I would love to contribute to the democrasy of this country. I imagine it must be hard. I always have simpathy for the candidate that loses, regardless of whether they are a demokrat or a republican. If I became a civil servant, I would hope to develop telapathy so I could know what the public really wanted.

1. _____ 2. _____ 3. _____

4. _____ 5. _____

Writing Activity

What would you like to be when you grow up? Write a short paragraph about the career you would like to pursue, and steps you think you would need to take to obtain it. Use five spelling words.

_____

_____

_____

_____

_____

_____

_____

_____

_____

_____

_____

_____

Name_____

Look at the words in each set below. One word in each set is spelled correctly. Use a pencil to fill in the circle next to the correct word. Before you begin, look at the sample set of words. Sample A has been done for you. Do Sample B by yourself. When you are sure you know what to do, you may go on with the rest of the page.

Sample A:

Ⓐ illegal
Ⓑ ilegall
Ⓒ ellegal
Ⓓ illegell

Sample B:

Ⓔ collect
Ⓕ colect
Ⓖ collectt
Ⓗ kollect

1. Ⓐ sympathy
   Ⓑ simpathy
   Ⓒ smmpathy
   Ⓓ sympathee

6. Ⓔ musishon
   Ⓕ muscishion
   Ⓖ musisian
   Ⓗ musician

11. Ⓐ demmocracy
    Ⓑ dumocracy
    Ⓒ democracy
    Ⓓ demokracy

16. Ⓔ apallogy
    Ⓕ apology
    Ⓖ appology
    Ⓗ apologee

2. Ⓔ pianist
   Ⓕ peanist
   Ⓖ pianisst
   Ⓗ peanisst

7. Ⓐ pollitician
   Ⓑ politician
   Ⓒ politishon
   Ⓓ polotician

12. Ⓔ arkeology
    Ⓕ archeology
    Ⓖ archaology
    Ⓗ archaeology

17. Ⓐ zology
    Ⓑ zoollogy
    Ⓒ zoology
    Ⓓ soology

3. Ⓐ fysician
   Ⓑ phisician
   Ⓒ physician
   Ⓓ physishon

8. Ⓔ turist
   Ⓕ tourist
   Ⓖ turrist
   Ⓗ tourest

13. Ⓐ ekology
    Ⓑ eckology
    Ⓒ eecology
    Ⓓ ecology

18. Ⓔ technology
    Ⓕ tecknology
    Ⓖ tecnology
    Ⓗ tecchnolgy

4. Ⓔ novelist
   Ⓕ novalist
   Ⓖ novulist
   Ⓗ novellist

9. Ⓐ geeologist
   Ⓑ jeologist
   Ⓒ geolojist
   Ⓓ geologist

14. Ⓔ biologist
    Ⓕ byologist
    Ⓖ biolugist
    Ⓗ bioligist

19. Ⓐ tecknician
    Ⓑ technician
    Ⓒ teccnision
    Ⓓ teknician

5. Ⓐ tellepathy
   Ⓑ telepethy
   Ⓒ telepathy
   Ⓓ tellpethy

10. Ⓔ speculist
    Ⓕ speciallist
    Ⓖ speshalist
    Ⓗ specialist

15. Ⓐ heroesm
    Ⓑ heroism
    Ⓒ heroizm
    Ⓓ herroism

20. Ⓔ demmucrat
    Ⓕ democrat
    Ⓖ demokrat
    Ⓗ democratt

Name _____

Fold back the paper along the dotted line. Write the words in the blanks as they are read aloud. When you finish the test, unfold the paper. Use the list at the right to correct any spelling mistakes.

1. _____
2. _____
3. _____
4. _____
5. _____
6. _____
7. _____
8. _____
9. _____
10. _____
11. _____
12. _____
13. _____
14. _____
15. _____
16. _____
17. _____
18. _____
19. _____
20. _____

Review Words 21. _____
22. _____
23. _____

Challenge Words 24. _____
25. _____

1. iris
2. nectar
3. cosmetics
4. chaos
5. solar
6. geography
7. mania
8. titanic
9. romance
10. geometry
11. helicopter
12. nocturnal
13. psychology
14. phobia
15. terrain
16. amnesia
17. tantalize
18. hygiene
19. mercury
20. marathon
21. musician
22. democracy
23. sympathy
24. lethal
25. hypnotize

At Home: Help the student practice the words he or she missed to prepare for the Posttest.

Name_____

Using the Word Study Steps

1. LOOK at the word.

2. SAY the word aloud.

3. STUDY the letters in the word.

4. WRITE the word.

5. CHECK the word.
   Did you spell the word right?
   If not, go back to step 1.

Missing Letters

Fill in the missing letters to form spelling words.

1. _____ metry

2. hyg _____

3. ter _____

4. _____ tar

5. _____ ology

6. ch _____ s

7. mara _____

8. ir _____

9. ti _____ ic

10. tanta _____

11. cos _____ ics

12. geo _____ y

13. mer _____

14. _____ urnal

15. ro _____ ce

16. ocean _____

17. so _____

18. _____ bia

19. _____ sia

20. heli _____ ter

Write the Words

Use the lines below to practice writing the spelling words.

_____ _____ _____ _____

_____ _____ _____ _____

_____ _____ _____ _____

_____ _____ _____ _____

At Home: Review the Word Study Steps to help the student spell new words.

Name_____

iris	nectar	cosmetics	chaos	solar
geography	oceanic	titanic	romance	geometry
helicopter	nocturnal	psychology	phobia	terrain
amnesia	tantalize	hygiene	mercury	marathon

Alphabetical Order

Write the spelling words in alphabetical order.

1. _____   11. _____
2. _____   12. _____
3. _____   13. _____
4. _____   14. _____
5. _____   15. _____
6. _____   16. _____
7. _____   17. _____
8. _____   18. _____
9. _____   19. _____
10. _____   20. _____

Write About It

Use ten of the spelling words above in a short piece of writing about a topic of your choice.

_____

_____

_____

_____

_____

_____

Name_____

iris	nectar	cosmetics	chaos	solar
geography	oceanic	titanic	romance	geometry
helicopter	nocturnal	psychology	phobia	terrain
amnesia	tantalize	hygiene	mercury	marathon

Word Meanings

Write the spelling word that matches each definition.

1. active at night _____

2. concern for personal cleanliness and health _____

3. fear of, or anxiety about something _____

4. colored part of the eye _____

5. extraordinary in size or strength _____

6. aircraft that moves with spinning blades _____

7. state of complete disorder or confusion _____

8. taking place in a large amount of water _____

9. chemical element found in thermometers _____

10. loss of memory _____

11. sweet liquid from flowers _____

12. love affair _____

13. concerning the sun _____

14. long distance running race _____

15. scientific study of human behavior _____

16. the study of the earth _____

17. to tease _____

18. beauty products _____

© Macmillan/McGraw-Hill

Name

There are five spelling mistakes in the paragraph below. Circle the misspelled words. Write the words correctly on the lines below.

Mr. Casey asked his students to write essays on what they felt has been the greatest invention of all time. Hakeem wrote about the helicoptar, even though he had never been in one. Sharon wrote about cosmetiks, even though her mother wouldn't let her wear any. Petra felt that advances in personal hygeene were important, but she had a germ phobea. Mr. Casey found many of the class's essays tanttalizzing, but claimed that the printing press was the most important invention because without it, we wouldn't have books or the ability to share ideas.

1. _____   2. _____   3. _____

4. _____   5. _____

Writing Activity

What do you think is the most important contribution to modern society? Write a paragraph describing something you think is essential to the way we live. Use five spelling words.

_____

_____

_____

_____

_____

_____

_____

_____

Name_____

Look at the words in each set below. One word in each set is spelled correctly. Use a pencil to fill in the circle next to the correct word. Before you begin, look at the sample set of words. Sample A has been done for you. Do Sample B by yourself. When you are sure you know what to do, you may go on with the rest of the page.

Sample A:

Ⓐ democracy
Ⓑ demmocracy
Ⓒ dimocracy
Ⓓ democracee

Sample B:

Ⓔ simpathee
Ⓕ symmpathy
Ⓖ sympathy
Ⓗ cympathy

1. Ⓐ irris
   Ⓑ iras
   Ⓒ irriss
   Ⓓ iris

2. Ⓔ geeometree
   Ⓕ geometree
   Ⓖ geometry
   Ⓗ jeometry

3. Ⓐ cozmetics
   Ⓑ cossmetucs
   Ⓒ cosmmetics
   Ⓓ cosmetics

4. Ⓔ tanntalize
   Ⓕ tanntalise
   Ⓖ tantalize
   Ⓗ tantalise

5. Ⓐ nokturnal
   Ⓑ noctirnal
   Ⓒ nocturnal
   Ⓓ nawcturnal

6. Ⓔ geography
   Ⓕ geeographee
   Ⓖ geographye
   Ⓗ gegraphy

7. Ⓐ fobia
   Ⓑ phobia
   Ⓒ phoobia
   Ⓓ phobea

8. Ⓔ teraine
   Ⓕ terrain
   Ⓖ terrane
   Ⓗ tirrain

9. Ⓐ kaos
   Ⓑ chaoss
   Ⓒ khaos
   Ⓓ chaos

10. Ⓔ marathon
    Ⓕ marrathon
    Ⓖ maratthon
    Ⓗ maruthon

11. Ⓐ psichology
    Ⓑ psychology
    Ⓒ pssychology
    Ⓓ psykology

12. Ⓔ mania
    Ⓕ mannia
    Ⓖ mannea
    Ⓗ manea

13. Ⓐ helacopter
    Ⓑ helicoptir
    Ⓒ helicopter
    Ⓓ helicoppter

14. Ⓔ hygiene
    Ⓕ higene
    Ⓖ hyjene
    Ⓗ hygene

15. Ⓐ solir
    Ⓑ sollar
    Ⓒ soler
    Ⓓ solar

16. Ⓔ rowmance
    Ⓕ rommance
    Ⓖ romance
    Ⓗ romanse

17. Ⓐ nektarr
    Ⓑ nectur
    Ⓒ nectir
    Ⓓ nectar

18. Ⓔ mercury
    Ⓕ merckury
    Ⓖ merrcury
    Ⓗ merkury

19. Ⓐ titanic
    Ⓑ titanick
    Ⓒ tittanic
    Ⓓ titannic

20. Ⓔ amnezia
    Ⓕ amnesia
    Ⓖ ammnesia
    Ⓗ anmnesia

© Macmillan/McGraw-Hill

Name_____

Fold back the paper along the dotted line. Write the words in the blanks as they are read aloud. When you finish the test, unfold the paper. Use the list at the right to correct any spelling mistakes.

1. _____	**1.** bazaar
2. _____	**2.** bronco
3. _____	**3.** sombrero
4. _____	**4.** caribou
5. _____	**5.** denim
6. _____	**6.** gong
7. _____	**7.** plaza
8. _____	**8.** igloo
9. _____	**9.** pizza
10. _____	**10.** barbecue
11. _____	**11.** canoe
12. _____	**12.** chocolate
13. _____	**13.** pajamas
14. _____	**14.** plateau
15. _____	**15.** poodle
16. _____	**16.** apricot
17. _____	**17.** balcony
18. _____	**18.** yacht
19. _____	**19.** cruise
20. _____	**20.** ballet
Review Words 21. _____	**21.** solar
22. _____	**22.** geography
23. _____	**23.** marathon
Challenge Words 24. _____	**24.** gondola
25. _____	**25.** kindergarten

At Home: Help the student practice the words he or she missed to prepare for the Posttest.

Name_____

Using the Word Study Steps

1. LOOK at the word.

2. SAY the word aloud.

3. STUDY the letters in the word.

4. WRITE the word.

5. CHECK the word.
   Did you spell the word right?
   If not, go back to step 1.

Missing Vowels

Fill in the missing vowels to form spelling words.

1. ch ___ c ___ l ___ t ___

2. ___ gl ___ ___

3. c ___ r ___ b ___ ___

4. y ___ cht

5. p ___ ___ dl ___

6. b ___ rb ___ c ___ ___

7. g ___ ng

8. br ___ nc ___

9. b ___ ll ___ t

10. b ___ z ___ ___ r

11. pl ___ t ___ ___ ___

12. pl ___ z ___

13. s ___ mbr ___ r ___

14. cr ___ ___ s ___

15. ___ pr ___ c ___ t

16. c ___ n ___ ___

17. d ___ n ___ m

18. p ___ j ___ m ___ s

19. b ___ lc ___ ny

20. p ___ zz ___

Make a Puzzle

Make up a puzzle of your own using the space on this page. Give it to someone else to solve. Be sure to include at least five spelling words in your puzzle.

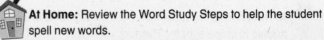

At Home: Review the Word Study Steps to help the student spell new words.

© Macmillan/McGraw-Hill

Name _____

bazaar	bronco	sombrero	caribou	denim
gong	plaza	igloo	pizza	barbecue
canoe	chocolate	pajamas	plateau	poodle
apricot	balcony	yacht	cruise	ballet

Sort the spelling words by number of syllables.

one

1. _____

2. _____

3. _____

two

4. _____

5. _____

6. _____

7. _____

8. _____

9. _____

10. _____

11. _____

12. _____

13. _____

three

14. _____

15. _____

16. _____

17. _____

18. _____

19. _____

20. _____

Name_____

bazaar	bronco	sombrero	caribou	denim
gong	plaza	igloo	pizza	barbecue
canoe	chocolate	pajamas	plateau	poodle
apricot	balcony	yacht	cruise	ballet

Finish the Set

Write the spelling word or words that belong in each group.

1. jeans, dungaree, _____
2. terrace, veranda, _____
3. retriever, collie, _____
4. tap, salsa, _____
5. market, fair, _____
6. valley, mountain, _____
7. teepee, townhouse, _____
8. vanilla, strawberry, _____
9. marketplace, town square, _____
10. derby, panama, _____
11. nightgown, lingerie, _____
12. slice, pepperoni, _____
13. deer, buck, _____
14. boat, kayak _____
15. orange, apple, _____
16. boat, ship, _____

© Macmillan/McGraw-Hill

Name_____

There are five spelling mistakes in the paragraph below. Circle the misspelled words. Write the words correctly on the lines below.

Last night I had the strangest dream. I was walking my poodal and all of sudden a large gonga in the center of the town plasa began to ring, alerting everyone that the volcano was preparing to erupt. I ran home, packed my paagamuz, and headed out of town. I was scared that if I stuck around I would wind up like barbacue from the lava of the volcano.

1. _____   2. _____   3. _____

4. _____   5. _____

Writing Activity

Have you ever had a really silly dream? Write a short story about it. Use at least five spelling words.

_____

_____

_____

_____

_____

_____

_____

_____

_____

_____

_____

_____

Name_____

Look at the words in each set below. One word in each set is spelled correctly. Use a pencil to fill in the circle next to the correct word. Before you begin, look at the sample set of words. Sample A has been done for you. Do Sample B by yourself. When you are sure you know what to do, you may go on with the rest of the page.

Sample A:

Ⓐ jeeography
Ⓑ geographee
Ⓒ geography
Ⓓ geogruphy

Sample B:

Ⓔ marrathon
Ⓕ maratthon
Ⓖ marathon
Ⓗ maruthon

1. Ⓐ bazar
   Ⓑ bazzar
   Ⓒ bazaar
   Ⓓ baazar

2. Ⓔ barbecue
   Ⓕ baarbekue
   Ⓖ barbecew
   Ⓗ barbbecue

3. Ⓐ somebrero
   Ⓑ sommbrero
   Ⓒ sombrrero
   Ⓓ sombrero

4. Ⓔ pllaza
   Ⓕ plaza
   Ⓖ plazza
   Ⓗ plasa

5. Ⓐ dennim
   Ⓑ denum
   Ⓒ denim
   Ⓓ denimm

6. Ⓔ gong
   Ⓕ gawng
   Ⓖ gonng
   Ⓗ gongg

7. Ⓐ paajamas
   Ⓑ pajamazz
   Ⓒ pajamas
   Ⓓ pajamus

8. Ⓔ kanoo
   Ⓕ canew
   Ⓖ canoe
   Ⓗ caneoe

9. Ⓐ apricot
   Ⓑ aprikot
   Ⓒ appricot
   Ⓓ apricott

10. Ⓔ yacht
    Ⓕ yaacht
    Ⓖ yachit
    Ⓗ yackt

11. Ⓐ piza
    Ⓑ pezza
    Ⓒ pessa
    Ⓓ pizza

12. Ⓔ plaatoe
    Ⓕ plateau
    Ⓖ platoe
    Ⓗ platteau

13. Ⓐ egloo
    Ⓑ igloo
    Ⓒ iglew
    Ⓓ iggloo

14. Ⓔ kariboo
    Ⓕ carribou
    Ⓖ caribuo
    Ⓗ caribou

15. Ⓐ crewse
    Ⓑ cruise
    Ⓒ criuse
    Ⓓ cruize

16. Ⓔ pewdle
    Ⓕ poodle
    Ⓖ poodel
    Ⓗ poodell

17. Ⓐ bronko
    Ⓑ broncco
    Ⓒ bronnco
    Ⓓ bronco

18. Ⓔ chocolate
    Ⓕ chokolate
    Ⓖ chawcolate
    Ⓗ chockolate

19. Ⓐ ballcony
    Ⓑ balkony
    Ⓒ balcony
    Ⓓ balcoknee

20. Ⓔ balet
    Ⓕ ballett
    Ⓖ ballat
    Ⓗ ballet

Name

Read each sentence. If an underlined word is spelled wrong, fill in the circle that goes with that word. If no word is spelled wrong, fill in the circle below NONE. Read Sample A, and do Sample B.

A. The winner of the <u>marathon</u> took a <u>cruise</u> on a <u>yaht</u>.
                  A   B   C

                                              NONE
A. Ⓐ Ⓑ Ⓒ Ⓓ

B. It is <u>illegal</u> to hunt <u>cariboo</u> on the <u>plateau</u>.
           E   F   G

                                              NONE
B. Ⓔ Ⓕ Ⓖ Ⓗ

1. The <u>politisian</u> was <u>impatiently</u> waiting in a <u>suburb</u>.
           A   B   C

                                              NONE
1. Ⓐ Ⓑ Ⓒ Ⓓ

2. Each <u>co-worker</u> gets a <u>commission</u> on the order they
             E   F

<u>submit</u>.
 G

                                              NONE
2. Ⓔ Ⓕ Ⓖ Ⓗ

3. The <u>balkony</u> was built to <u>accommodate</u> a <u>barbecue</u> grill.
           A   B   C

                                              NONE
3. Ⓐ Ⓑ Ⓒ Ⓓ

4. A <u>postwar</u> country had a <u>transformation</u> to a <u>democracee</u>.
         E   F   G

                                              NONE
4. Ⓔ Ⓕ Ⓖ Ⓗ

5. The <u>geologist</u> used a <u>submarin</u> to explore <u>oceanic</u> waves.
           A   B   C

                                              NONE
5. Ⓐ Ⓑ Ⓒ Ⓓ

6. The pilot and <u>copilot</u> must <u>cooperate</u> to fly the
                     E   F

<u>helicoptar</u>.
   G

                                              NONE
6. Ⓔ Ⓕ Ⓖ Ⓗ

7. The <u>geography</u> class had to <u>collect</u> samples from the
                A   B

<u>terraine</u>.
  C

                                              NONE
7. Ⓐ Ⓑ Ⓒ Ⓓ

8. The <u>bilogist</u> was a <u>specialist</u> in the <u>profession</u>.
         E   F   G

                                              NONE
8. Ⓔ Ⓕ Ⓖ Ⓗ

9. The <u>democrat</u> gave a speech to the <u>assembly</u> on her
          A   B

plans to change <u>immigration</u> laws.
                    C

                                            NONE
9. Ⓐ Ⓑ Ⓒ Ⓓ

10. The <u>archeologist</u> was to <u>accompany</u> her <u>companion</u> to
    E   F   G
    the formal dinner.

    NONE
    10. Ⓔ Ⓕ Ⓖ Ⓗ

11. The <u>novelist</u> was happy to <u>anounce</u> the release of her
    A   B
    new <u>romance</u> guide.
        C

    NONE
    11. Ⓐ Ⓑ Ⓒ Ⓓ

12. Is it bad <u>hygene</u> to eat <u>pizza</u> in your <u>pajamas</u>?
              E   F   G

    NONE
    12. Ⓔ Ⓕ Ⓖ Ⓗ

13. The <u>pianist</u> worked with another <u>musician</u> to write the
    A   B
    score for the <u>ballet</u>.
                  C

    NONE
    13. Ⓐ Ⓑ Ⓒ Ⓓ

14. In the chef's special dessert he decided to <u>combine</u>
                                                E
    <u>apricot</u> with <u>chocolat</u>.
    F   G

    NONE
    14. Ⓔ Ⓕ Ⓖ Ⓗ

15. The <u>torist</u> had never seen an <u>igloo</u> or a <u>canoe</u>.
    A   B   C

    NONE
    15. Ⓐ Ⓑ Ⓒ Ⓓ

16. At the <u>bazaar</u>, I bought a <u>sombrero</u> and a plastic <u>bronco</u>.
    E   F   G

    NONE
    16. Ⓔ Ⓕ Ⓖ Ⓗ

17. The <u>fysician</u> checked the <u>iris</u> of my eye, and took my
    A   B
    temperature with a thermometer filled with <u>mercury</u>.
                                               C

    NONE
    17. Ⓐ Ⓑ Ⓒ Ⓓ

18. After his <u>arrest</u> he decided to <u>postpon</u> his <u>apology</u>.
              E   F   G

    NONE
    18. Ⓔ Ⓕ Ⓖ Ⓗ

19. The community could not <u>suppress</u> their <u>suport</u> for
                           A   B
    her brave act of <u>heroism</u>.
                     C

    NONE
    19. Ⓐ Ⓑ Ⓒ Ⓓ

20. The <u>poodle</u> liked the <u>nectar</u> of the flowers planted in
    E   F
    the garden at the <u>plaza</u>.
                      G

    NONE
    20. Ⓔ Ⓕ Ⓖ Ⓗ

CURRICULUM